GEOMETRY

Homework Helper

Carnegie Learning™

THE COGNITIVE TUTOR® COMPANY

Carnegie Learning™
THE COGNITIVE TUTOR® COMPANY

Pittsburgh, PA
Phone 888.851.7094
Fax 412.690.2444

www.carnegielearning.com

Acknowledgements

We would like to thank those listed below who helped to
prepare the Cognitive Tutor® *Geometry* Homework Helper.

Michael Amick
Michele Covatto
The Carnegie Learning Development Team

Geometry was used to design the archways that form the tunnel on the front cover.
The perspective of the photograph is very interesting. It appears as though the archways
continue to get smaller as you go through the tunnel. Actually, each archway is the same size.
This is because a three-dimensional object, the tunnel, is being represented on a two-dimensional
surface, the cover of this book. Each archway is a half of a circle, or a semicircle. To design the
tunnel, architects used the formula for the circumference of a semicircle, which is the formula
shown on the cover. As you work through the Cognitive Tutor Geometry text and software,
you will see additional opportunities for using Geometry in your everyday activities.

ISBN-13 978-1-932409-70-3
ISBN-10 1-932409-70-X
Homework Helper

Printed in the United States of America
1-2006-VH
2-2006-VH
3-2006-VH
4-2007-VH
5-2007-VH
6-4/2008-HPS

Introduction

Welcome to Carnegie Learning's Cognitive Tutor® *Geometry* curriculum!
We are excited that your student will be part of our unique approach to learning mathematics.

A Better Approach to Mathematics for Your Student

Research and field tests have validated that Carnegie Learning's approach helps students to improve their course grades and overall achievement. Whether your student excels in or struggles with mathematics, the Cognitive Tutor *Geometry* curriculum will help your student strengthen skills, content knowledge, and confidence.

The curriculum uses a scientifically-researched approach based on 20 years of investigation into how students think, learn, and apply new knowledge in mathematics. Based on extensive research and design at Carnegie Mellon University and field-tested by leading mathematics educators, our approach uses students' intuitive problem solving abilities as a powerful bridge to a more formal understanding of mathematics.

Software and Textbook Blended Curriculum

The Cognitive Tutor *Geometry* curriculum is a blended curriculum in which the software and text components compliment one another. Your student will spend about 40% of class instructional time using computer-based tutorials and 60% using the *Student Text* to collaborate with peers and work with his or her teacher.

Students work at their own pace in the software component of the curriculum. The learning system is built on *cognitive models,* which represent the knowledge that a student might possess about the mathematics that they are studying. The software assesses students' prior mathematical knowledge on a step-by-step basis and presents problems tailored to their individual skill levels.

Using the Cognitive Tutor *Geometry* software, your student will receive the benefits of individualized instruction, ample practice, immediate feedback, and coaching. Just-in-Time Hints, On-Demand Hints, and positive reinforcement will put your student in control of his or her own learning.

The Cognitive Tutor *Geometry Student Text* offers lessons that parallel and extend the development of concepts in the software. The lessons emphasize written analyses and classroom presentations. Your student will engage in problem solving and reasoning, and will communicate using multiple representations of math concepts. The *Student Text* provides an opportunity for analysis, extended investigation, and the exploration of alternate solution paths. Real-world situations are used in problems designed to emphasize conceptual understanding. The goal of the *Student Text* is to be engaging and effective so your student will have fun while "Learning by Doing."

A Closer Look at the Cognitive Tutor Geometry Software

Skills for the Real World   Because people draw on basic mathematical reasoning skills for common tasks such as finding the distance across a river, estimating the height of a building, planning a garden, or calculating the perimeter of a window, these types of problems form the core of the Cognitive Tutor *Geometry* software.

Monitoring and Feedback   The Cognitive Tutor *Geometry* software monitors student activities as they work and provides them with feedback to individualize instruction. If a student makes an error, for example, the software will indicate why the answer is incorrect, or pose a thought-provoking question to redirect the student's reasoning. Through individualized feedback, the software keeps students on task, marks progress, and gives students a sense of accomplishment. The software also identifies areas in which a student is having difficulty and presents the student with problems that target those specific skills.

Optimizing Classroom Time   By individualizing instruction and targeting each student's strengths and weaknesses, the Cognitive Tutor *Geometry* software can maximize the effectiveness of both the student's and the teacher's use of classroom time. The software immediately shows students whether their problem solving strategies and mathematical skills will be successful, allowing them to focus on correcting errors and developing skills that they find difficult. By using the diagnostic tools that accompany the software, teachers are free to interact with students on an individual basis and to target struggling students.

A Closer Look at the Cognitive Tutor Geometry Student Text

Multiple Representations   Throughout the Cognitive Tutor *Geometry* Student Text, deliberate connections are made between different representations in mathematics. For instance, students are shown that tables, graphs, and equations are different ways to represent functions.

Collaborative Learning Focus   The *Student Text* emphasizes the collaborative learning instruction model. Icons are placed at the beginning of problems in the lessons that encourage working in partner teams and in small groups. The instructional model icons are:

- Discuss to Understand
- Think for Yourself
- Work with Your Partner
- Work with Your Group
- Share with the Class

A Typical Week in a Cognitive Tutor Geometry Classroom

The Cognitive Tutor *Geometry* classroom is a dynamic, adaptive environment. While no two weeks will be exactly the same in the Cognitive Tutor *Geometry* classroom, most weeks will be split between classroom activities and work in the computer lab. The number of sessions of each type that the teacher schedules depends on the teacher's preference and the availability of lab time. Carnegie Learning suggests that students spend 40% of their class time in the computer lab working with the computer and 60% with *Student Text* investigations. Below is an itinerary outlining a typical mid-semester week.

Monday

- Students complete the *Student Text* investigation started on Friday with group presentations.

- Teacher solicits questions on the completed investigation and wraps up the investigation by asking questions that lead students to reflect on the material covered.

- Students begin a new *Student Text* investigation.

Tuesday

- Students complete about half of the investigation started on Monday.

- Teacher has students respond to a writing prompt to summarize their work.

Wednesday

- Students work with the software in the computer lab.

Thursday

- Students complete the investigation started on Tuesday.

- Partners present their findings of Tuesday's investigation using a written format.

- Teacher solicits questions and comments on the completed investigation, wraps up the investigation by asking questions that lead students to apply their knowledge of the material covered.

Friday

- Students work with the software in the computer lab.

How to Use the Homework Helper

The Homework Helper includes a practice page for each lesson in your student's *Student Text*. The page includes a worked example of the skills covered in the lesson. You may review the example with your student or have the student try the example without seeing the solution, and then review the example together.

Each page of the Homework Helper also has practice exercises that your student can try. The answers to the exercises are included at the back of the Homework Helper. Encourage your student to complete the solution before looking at the answer.

You can help your student to understand important mathematics vocabulary by reviewing the key words in a lesson.

Other Ways to Help Your Student

Encourage your student to share what he or she has been doing in mathematics class by showing you the lessons of his or her *Student Text*.

Support your student in completing his or her homework regularly by creating a consistent homework time each evening.

Use praise to encourage your student that he or she will succeed through persistent effort in working on the homework assignments.

Carnegie Learning's Ongoing Support

Teacher Training Teacher Training gives educators the opportunity to understand the philosophy and application of the Carnegie Learning approach to mathematics. The training also provides important insights into the Cognitive Tutor *Geometry* curriculum's pedagogical, implementation, and assessment features.

Training sessions are conducted by Certified Implementation Specialists (CISs). Every CIS is a current or former mathematics teacher who has completed in-depth training from Carnegie Learning's staff of educators, technology specialists, and curriculum developers.

Family Math Night Carnegie Learning offers families the opportunity to become involved through special programs such as our Family Math Night, in which parents come into their student's classroom to experience first-hand how the Cognitive Tutor *Geometry* curriculum helps students learn mathematics. Students and their teachers work together to assist parents in solving mathematics problems using the Cognitive Tutor *Geometry* software and *Student Text* investigation.

Introduction

Contents

5 Parallel and Perpendicular Lines

6 Simple Transformations

7 Similarity

8 Congruence

Building a Deck

Introduction to Polygons, Perimeter, and Area

Students should be able to answer these questions after Lesson 1.1:

■ How are polygons named?

■ How is perimeter calculated?

■ What is the relationship between perimeter and area?

Directions

Read Question 1 and its solution. Then complete Questions 2 through 4.

1. A homeowner is designing a small tiled patio for her backyard. She will need to purchase 1-foot by 1-foot square tiles for the patio, and a fence to put along the border of the patio. Because cost is a factor, she is considering several options. If the patio is a 10-foot by 12-foot rectangle, how many feet of fencing should she buy? How many tiles should she buy?

   Step 1 The distance around a figure is the perimeter. The perimeter is calculated by finding the sum of the lengths of the sides. So, the perimeter is 10 + 12 + 10 + 12 = 44 feet.

   Step 2 Each tile is one square foot. Because the patio is 10 feet by 12 feet, she should buy 120 tiles. Note that it may be helpful to draw a picture when calculating area and perimeter.

2. Suppose that the patio is a rectangle that is 12 feet by 16 feet. How many feet of fencing should she buy? How many tiles should she buy?

3. Suppose that the patio is a rectangle that is 13 feet by 8 feet. How many feet of fencing should she buy? How many tiles should she buy?

4. Suppose that a homeowner has only enough money to purchase 100 square feet of tile. What patio dimensions would require the least amount of fencing?

1.2 Weaving a Rug
Area and Perimeter of a Rectangle and Area of a Parallelogram

Students should be able to answer these questions after Lesson 1.2:
- How do you find the area of a rectangle?
- How do you find the area of a parallelogram?
- How do you find the perimeter of a polygon?

Directions

Read Question 1 and its solution. Then complete Questions 2 through 5.

1. The cost of carpet is determined by calculating the number of square feet that will be needed to cover a floor. How many square feet of carpet will be needed to cover a rectangular room with a length of 20 feet and a width of 12 feet?

   Step 1 In the previous lesson, you estimated the area by counting the squares on a grid. In this lesson, you discovered the formulas that can be used to determine the area of a rectangle (Area = Length × Width) and the area of a parallelogram (Area = Base × Height).

   Step 2 The amount of carpet needed to cover the room is 20 × 12 = 240 square feet.

2. How many square feet of carpet will be needed to cover a rectangular room that is 8 feet by 11 feet?

3. How many square feet of carpet will be needed to cover a rectangular room that is 13 feet by 9 feet?

4. How many square feet of carpet will be needed to cover a rectangular room that is 12 feet by 12 feet?

5. How many square feet of carpet will be needed to cover a room shaped like a parallelogram with a base of 10 feet and height of 9 feet?

© 2008 Carnegie Learning, Inc.

Sailboat Racing

Area of a Triangle

Students should be able to answer these questions after Lesson 1.3:
- How do you find the area of a triangle?
- How can unknown measures for base and height be determined when the area of a triangle is known?

Directions

Read Question 1 and its solution. Then complete Questions 2 and 3.

1. When tiling floors, the area of many corners, closets, and odd spaces are in the shapes of triangles. When determining the area and cost for tiling a room, it is important to be able to use the formula for the area of a triangle. What is the area of a triangular region with a base of 3 feet and a height of 4 feet?

   Step 1 Recall that the area of a rectangle can be found by multiplying the base by the height. Because a rectangle can be divided into two equal triangles, the area of a triangle is exactly half the area of a rectangle. So, the formula for the area of a triangle is $A = \frac{1}{2}bh$.

   Step 2 The area of the triangular region is $\frac{1}{2}(3)(4) = 6$ square feet.

2. Find the area of a triangle with a base of 5 feet and a height of 2 feet.

3. Find the area of a triangle with a base of 10 yards and a height of 1 yard.

In Question 4, find the value of the variable in the area equation. Then complete Questions 5 through 7.

4. $30 = \frac{5h}{2}$

   Step 1 Multiply each side of the equation by 2. $60 = 5h$

   Step 2 Divide each side of the equation by 5. $12 = h$

5. $10 = \frac{b(4)}{2}$

6. $21 = \frac{(b)6}{2}$

7. $\frac{3h}{2} = 24$

The Keystone Effect

Area of a Trapezoid

Students should be able to answer these questions after Lesson 1.4:

■ How do you find the area of a trapezoid?

■ How can unknown measures for the base and height be determined when the area of a trapezoid is known?

Directions

Read Question 1 and its solution. Then complete Questions 2 through 4.

1. Find the area of a trapezoid with base lengths of 3 feet and 5 feet and a height of 6 feet.

   Step 1   Use the formula to find the area of a trapezoid. $A = \frac{1}{2}(b_1 + b_2)h$

   Step 2   Identify the bases and height of the trapezoid. $b_1 = 3$ feet; $b_2 = 5$ feet; $h = 6$ feet

   Step 3   Substitute the known values into the formula and evaluate.

   $$A = \frac{1}{2}(b_1 + b_2)h$$

   $$= \frac{1}{2}(3 + 5)6$$

   $$= 24$$

   The area of the trapezoid is 24 square feet.

2. Find the area of a trapezoid with base lengths 2 inches and 6 inches and a height of 5 inches.

3. Find the area of a trapezoid with base lengths 10 centimeters and 15 centimeters and a height of 8 centimeters.

4. Find the area of a trapezoid with base lengths 6 meters and 7 meters and a height of 2 meters.

Read Question 5 and its solution. Then complete Questions 6 and 7.

5. The area of a trapezoid is 42 square inches. The height of the trapezoid is 7 inches and the length of one base is 4 inches. Find the length of the other base.

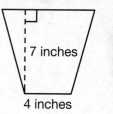

7 inches

4 inches

Step 1 Identify the known values. $A = 42$ square inches; $h = 7$ inches; $b_1 = 4$ inches.

Step 2 Substitute the known values into the formula for the area of a trapezoid.

$$A = \frac{1}{2}(b_1 + b_2)h$$

$$42 = \frac{1}{2}(4 + b_2)(7)$$

Step 3 Solve the equation for b_2.

$$6 = \frac{1}{2}(4 + b_2)$$

$$12 = 4 + b_2$$

$$8 = b_2$$

So, the length of the other base is 8 inches.

6. The area of a trapezoid is 99 square centimeters. The height is 9 centimeters and the length of one base is 12 centimeters. Find the length of the other base.

7. The area of a trapezoid is 72 square yards. The lengths of the bases are 3 yards and 9 yards. Find the height of the trapezoid.

Traffic Signs
Area of a Regular Polygon

Students should be able to answer these questions after Lesson 1.5:

- What is a regular polygon?
- How do you find the area of a regular polygon?

Directions

Read Question 1 and its solution. Then complete Questions 2 through 4.

1. Find the area of a regular hexagon with a side length of 8 centimeters and an apothem of about 7 centimeters.

   Step 1 A regular polygon is a polygon in which all sides are equal in length and all angles are equal in measure. The apothem of a regular polygon is the perpendicular distance from the center to a side. The apothem is the height of each triangle in the figure at the right.

   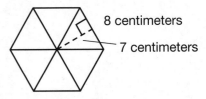

   8 centimeters

   7 centimeters

   Step 2 For regular polygons, calculate the area by dividing the figure into equal triangles. Simply find the area of one triangle, and then multiply the result by the number of triangles that make up the polygon. In the figure above, the area of each triangle is $\frac{1}{2}(8)(7) = 28$ square centimeters. There are six triangles in the hexagon, so the total area is $28(6) = 168$ square centimeters.

2. Find the area of a regular pentagon in which each side length is 6 feet and the apothem is about 4 feet.

3. Find the area of a regular octagon in which each side length is 5 centimeters and the apothem is about 6 centimeters.

4. Find the area of a regular nonagon in which each side length is 16 inches and the apothem is about 22 inches.

Photography

Circumference and Area of a Circle

Students should be able to answer this question after Lesson 1.6:
- How do you find the circumference of a circle?
- How do you find the area of a circle?

Directions

Read Question 1 and its solution. Then complete Questions 2 and 3.

1. Find the circumference of the circle shown at the right. Note that the circumference is the distance around the circle.

   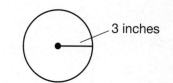

   Step 1 To find the circumference of a circle, use the formula $C = \pi d$, where C is the circumference of the circle and d is the diameter of the circle.

   Step 2 The radius of the circle is 5 inches. So, the diameter of the circle is 2 times the radius, or 10 inches.

   Step 3 Substitute the known values into the formula. $C = \pi(10)$

   Step 4 Use 3.14 for π. So, the circumference of the circle is about 31.4 inches.

2. Find the circumference of a circle with a radius of 7 centimeters.

3. Find the circumference of a circle with a diameter of 12 inches.

Read Question 4 and its solution. Then complete Questions 5 and 6.

4. Find the area of the circle shown at the right.

   Step 1 To find the area of a circle, use the formula $A = \pi r^2$, where A is the area and r is the radius of the circle.

   Step 2 Substitute the known values into the formula. $A = \pi(3)^2$

   Step 3 Use 3.14 for π. So, the area of the circle is about 28.26 square inches.

5. Find the area of a circle with a radius of 4 centimeters.

6. Find the area of a circle with a diameter of 20 inches.

Installing Carpeting and Tile

Composite Figures

Students should be able to answer these questions after Lesson 1.7:

■ What is a composite figure?

■ How do you find the area of a composite figure?

Directions

Read Question 1 and its solution. Then find the total area of the figures in Questions 2 and 3.

1. Find the area of the composite figure shown below.

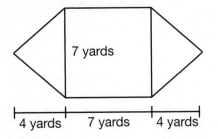

7 yards

4 yards   7 yards   4 yards

Step 1 The region is comprised of a square and two triangles. To find the total area, first find the area of each region that makes up the composite figure.

Step 2 The area of each triangle can be found by using the formula $A = \dfrac{1}{2}bh$.

So, the area of each triangle is $\dfrac{1}{2}(7)(4)$, or 14 square yards.

Step 3 The area of the square can be found by using the formula $A = \ell w$. So, the area of the square is (7)(7), or 49 square inches.

Step 4 The total area of the figure is the sum of the areas of the three regions. So, the total area is 14(2) + 49, or 77 square yards.

2.

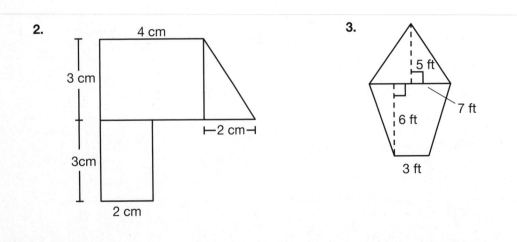

4 cm

3 cm

2 cm

3cm

2 cm

3.

5 ft

7 ft

6 ft

3 ft

© 2008 Carnegie Learning, Inc.

Backyard Barbecue

Introduction to Volume and Surface Area

Students should be able to answer these questions after Lesson 2.1:

■ What is the volume of a figure?

■ How does the volume of a figure differ from its surface area?

■ How do you find the volume and surface area of a figure?

Directions

Read Question 1 and its solution. Then find the volume and surface area of each figure in Questions 2 through 4.

1. Calculate the volume and the surface area of the figure shown at the right.

8 inches
4 inches
10 inches

Step 1   The formula for the volume of a rectangular prism is $V = \ell wh$ where ℓ is the length, w is the width, and h is the height. Because you are multiplying inches by inches by inches, the result is measured in cubic inches.

Step 2   Substitute the values from the figure into the formula.

$V = (10)(4)(8) = 320$

So, the volume of the figure is 320 cubic inches.

Step 3   The formula for surface area of a rectangular prism is Surface Area $= 2\ell w + 2\ell h + 2wh$, where ℓ is the length, w is the width, and h is the height. Because you are multiplying inches by inches, the result is measured in square inches.

Step 4   Substitute the values from the figure into the formula.

Surface Area $= 2(10)(4) + 2(10)(8) + 2(4)(8) = 80 + 160 + 64 = 304$

So, the surface area of the figure is 304 square inches.

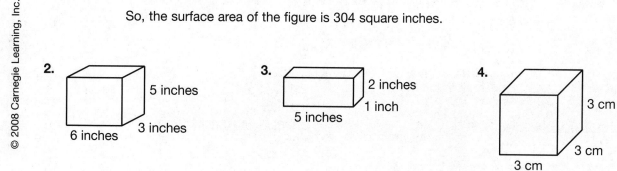

2.
5 inches
3 inches
6 inches

3.
2 inches
1 inch
5 inches

4.
3 cm
3 cm
3 cm

Turn Up the Volume
Volume of a Prism

Students should be able to answer this question after Lesson 2.2:

■ How do you find the volume of a prism?

Directions

Read Question 1 and its solution. Then find the volume of each figure in Questions 2 and 3.

2

1. Calculate the volume of the prism shown below. The base of the prism is shown below at the right.

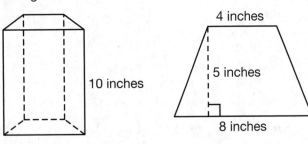

4 inches

5 inches

10 inches

8 inches

Step 1 To calculate the volume of a prism, use the formula $V = Bh$, where B is the area of the base and h is the height. First, find the area of the base of the prism.

The base is a trapezoid, so use the formula $A = \frac{1}{2}(b_1 + b_2)h$.

$$A = \frac{1}{2}(4 + 8)5 = 30$$

So, the area of the base of the prism is 30 square inches.

Step 2 Multiply the area of the base of the prism by the height of the prism to find the volume of the prism.

$$V = Bh$$

$$= (30)(10) = 300$$

So, the volume of the prism is 300 cubic inches.

2. Rectangular Prism

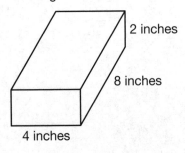

2 inches

8 inches

4 inches

3. Triangular Prism

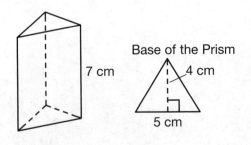

7 cm

Base of the Prism

4 cm

5 cm

Bending Light Beams
Surface Area of a Prism

Students should be able to answer these questions after Lesson 2.3:

- How do you find the surface area of a prism?
- What is the difference between the lateral area and the surface area?

Directions

Read Question 1 and its solution. Then find the surface area of each figure in Questions 2 and 3.

1. Calculate the surface area of the prism shown at the right.

   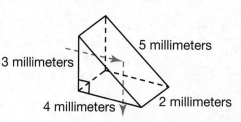

   5 millimeters

   3 millimeters

   4 millimeters   2 millimeters

   Step 1   Calculate the area of the bases (the two triangles).

   $A = \frac{1}{2}bh = \frac{1}{2}(4)(3) = 6$ square millimeters.

   Because there are two bases, the total area of the bases is 12 square millimeters.

   Step 2   Calculate the lateral area. The lateral area of this prism is made up of 3 rectangles.

   Lateral Area $= (2)(5) + (2)(4) + (2)(3) = 10 + 8 + 6 = 24$ square millimeters

   Step 3   Calculate the total surface area. The surface area is the sum of the lateral area and the area of the bases. So, the surface area of this prism is $12 + 24 = 36$ square millimeters.

2.

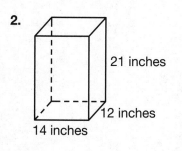

   21 inches

   12 inches

   14 inches

3.

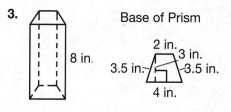

   Base of Prism

   8 in.

   2 in.

   3 in.

   3.5 in.   3.5 in.

   4 in.

2.4 Modern Day Pyramids
Volume of a Pyramid

Students should be able to answer this question after Lesson 2.4:

■ How do you find the volume of a pyramid?

Directions

Read Question 1 and its solution. Then find the volume of each figure in Questions 2 and 3.

1. Calculate the volume of the pyramid shown at the right.

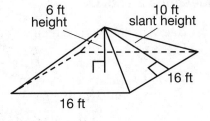

6 ft
height

10 ft
slant height

16 ft

16 ft

Step 1 In a pyramid, the height is the perpendicular distance from the vertex to the base.
The slant height is the altitude of the lateral faces. Find the area of the base.

$B = (16)(16) = 256$

So, the area of the base of the pyramid is 256 square units.

Step 2 Use the formula for a pyramid, $V = \frac{1}{3}Bh$ where B is the area of the base and h is the height.

$V = \frac{1}{3}Bh$

$= \frac{1}{3}(256)(6)$

$= 512$

So, the volume of the pyramid is 512 cubic feet.

2.

18 ft

20 ft

20 ft

3.

10 ft

3 ft   6 ft

Soundproofing

Surface Area of a Pyramid

Students should be able to answer these questions after Lesson 2.5:

- How do you find the surface area of a pyramid?
- How do you find the surface area of composite figures?

Directions

Read Question 1 and its solution. Then find the surface area of each figure in Questions 2 and 3.

1. Calculate the surface area of the pyramid shown at the right.

   Step 1 Calculate the area of the square base.

   $A = bh = (32)(32) = 1024$

   The area of the base is 1024 square inches.

   Step 2 Calculate the lateral area. The lateral area of this pyramid is made up of 4 triangles.

   The lateral area is $4\left(\dfrac{1}{2}\right)(32)(20) = 1280$ square inches.

   Step 3 Calculate the total surface area. The surface area is the sum of the lateral area and the area of the base, or $1024 + 1280 = 2304$ square inches. The surface area S of a regular pyramid can be found by using the formula $B + \dfrac{1}{2}P\ell$,

   where B is the area of the base, P is the perimeter of the base, and ℓ is the slant height of the pyramid.

2.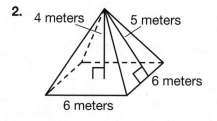

3.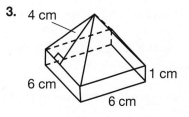

Making Concrete Stronger

Volume and Surface Area of a Cylinder

Students should be able to answer this question after Lesson 2.6:

■ How do you find the volume of a cylinder?

■ How do you find the surface area of a cylinder?

Directions

2

Read Question 1 and its solution. Then find the volume of the each figure in Questions 2 and 3.

1. Find the volume of the cylinder shown at the right.

   Step 1 The radius of the cylinder is 3 inches. The height of the cylinder is 7 inches. Use the formula for the volume of a cylinder, $V = \pi r^2 h$, where r is the radius and h is the height.

   Step 2 Substitute the values into the formula. Use 3.14 for π.

   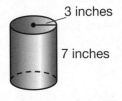
   3 inches
   7 inches

   $$V = \pi(3)^2(7)$$
   $$= 63\pi$$
   $$\approx 197.82$$

   So, the volume of the cylinder is about 197.82 cubic inches.

2. 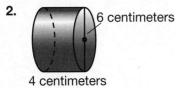 6 centimeters

    4 centimeters

3. 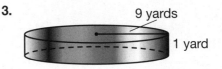 9 yards

    1 yard

Read Question 4 and its solution. Then find the surface area of each figure in Questions 5 and 6.

4. Find the surface area of the cylinder shown at the right.

   Step 1 The radius of the cylinder is 4 inches. The height of the cylinder is 10 inches. Use the formula for the surface area of a cylinder, $S = 2\pi r^2 + 2\pi rh$, where r is the radius and h is the height.

   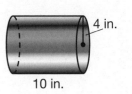
   4 in.
   10 in.

   Step 2 Substitute the values into the formula. Use 3.14 for π.

   $$S = 2\pi(4)^2 + 2\pi(4)(10)$$
   $$= 2\pi(16) + 80\pi$$
   $$\approx 351.68$$

   So, the surface area of the cylinder is about 351.68 square inches.

5.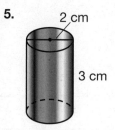

2 cm

3 cm

6. 5 ft

15 ft

2.7 Sand Piles

Volume and Surface Area of a Cone

Students should be able to answer these questions after Lesson 2.7:

■ How do you find the volume of a cone?

■ How do you find the surface area of a cone?

Directions

2

Read Question 1 and its solution. Then find the volume and surface area of each figure in Questions 2 and 3.

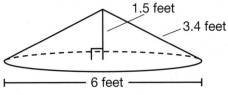

1. Calculate the volume and surface area of the cone shown at the right.

   Step 1 Identify the radius, height, and slant height of the cone.

   $r = 3$ feet, $h = 1.5$ feet, $\ell = 3.4$ feet

   Step 2 Substitute these values into the formula for the volume of a cone, $V = \frac{1}{3}\pi r^2 h$.

   $$V = \frac{1}{3}\pi(3)^2(1.5) = \frac{1}{3}(13.5)\pi = 4.5\pi$$

   So, the volume of the cone is about 14.13 cubic feet.

   Step 3 Substitute the values into the formula for the surface area of the cone, $SA = \pi r^2 + \pi r\ell$.

   $$SA = \pi(3)^2 + \pi(3)(3.4) = 9\pi + 10.2\pi = 19.2\pi$$

   So, the surface area of the cone is about 60.288 square feet.

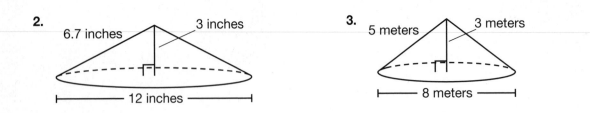

2.

3.

Ball Bearings and Motion
Volume and Surface Area of a Sphere

Students should be able to answer these questions after Lesson 2.8:

- How do you find the volume of a sphere?
- How do you find the surface area of a sphere?

Directions

Read Question 1 and its solution. Then find the volume and surface area of each figure in Questions 2 and 3.

1. Calculate the volume and surface area of the sphere shown at the right.

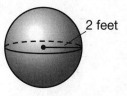
2 feet

   Step 1 Identify the radius of the sphere.

   $r = 2$ feet

   Step 2 Substitute this value into the formula for the volume

   of a sphere, $V = \frac{4}{3}\pi r^3$, where r is the radius.

   $$V = \frac{4}{3}\pi(2)^3 = \frac{4}{3}\pi(8) = \frac{32\pi}{3}$$

   So, the volume of the sphere is about 33.493 cubic feet.

   Step 3 Substitute the values into the formula for the surface area of the sphere, $SA = 4\pi r^2$, where r is the radius.

   $SA = 4\pi(2)^2 = 16\pi$

   So, the surface area of the sphere is about 50.24 square feet.

2.

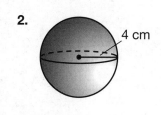
4 cm

3.

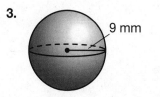
9 mm

2

Constellations

Naming, Measuring, and Classifying Angles

Students should be able to answer these questions after Lesson 3.1:

- How are words and symbols used to name lines, rays, and segments?
- How is an angle measured?
- How are angles classified?

Directions

Read Question 1 and its solution. Then name each object in Questions 2 and 3 by using words and symbols.

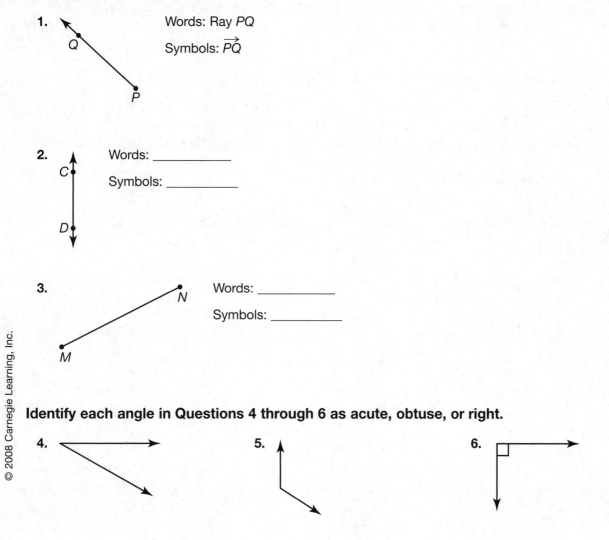

1. Words: Ray *PQ*

   Symbols: $\overrightarrow{PQ}$

2. Words: _____

   Symbols: _____

3. Words: _____

   Symbols: _____

Identify each angle in Questions 4 through 6 as acute, obtuse, or right.

4.

5.

6.

Cable-Stayed Bridges

Special Angles

Students should be able to answer these questions after Lesson 3.2:

- How are complementary and supplementary angles identified?
- How are adjacent angles and vertical angles identified?

Directions

Read Question 1 and its solution. Then complete Question 2.

1. Find the complement and supplement for an angle whose measure is 27°.

   Step 1 An angle and its complement have a sum of 90°. Let x be the measure of the complement. Write and solve an equation for x.

   $x + 27 = 90$

   So, the complement has a measure of 63°.

   Step 2 An angle and its supplement have a sum of 180°. Let x be the measure of the supplement. Write and solve an equation for x.

   $x + 27 = 180$

   So, the supplement has a measure of 153°.

2. Find the complement and supplement for an angle whose measure is 65°.

   Complement: _____   Supplement: _____

Read Question 3 and its solution. Then, find the measures of the angles in Question 4.

3. Identify one pair of vertical angles and one linear pair. Then find the measure of all angles in the diagram shown at the right.

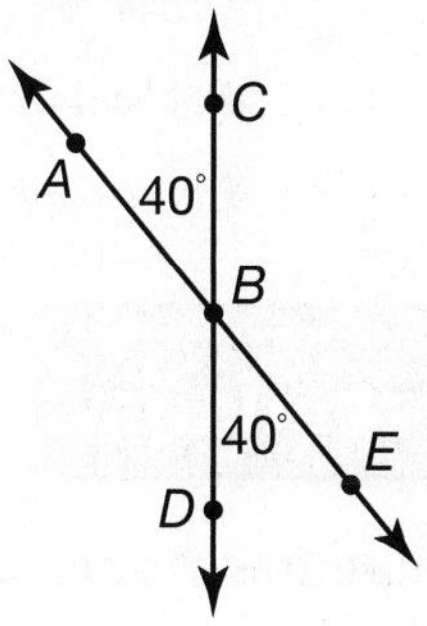

Step 1 *Vertical angles* are angles whose sides form two pairs of opposite rays. Angles *CBA* and *DBE* are vertical angles.

Step 2 Angles *CBE* and *EBD* form a *linear pair* because they are an adjacent pair of angles whose noncommon sides form opposite rays. Angles *EBD* and *DBA* also form a linear pair.

Step 3 The angles in a linear pair are supplementary.
So, $m\angle CBE = 180° - m\angle EBD = 180° - 40° = 140°$
and $m\angle DBA = 180° - m\angle EBD = 180° - 40° = 140°$.

4.

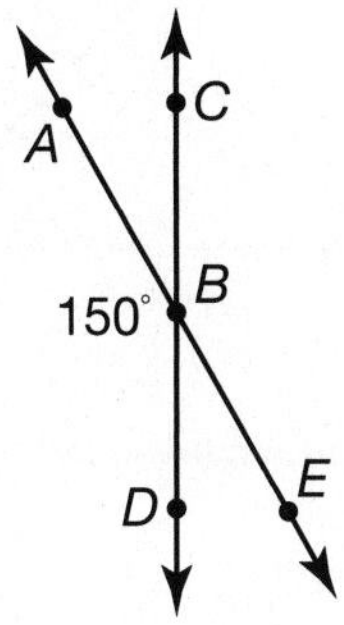

3.3 Designing a Kitchen
Angles of a Triangle

Students should be able to answer these questions after Lesson 3.3:
- How is the Triangle Sum Theorem used to determine angle measures?
- How is the Exterior Angle Sum Theorem used to determine angle measures?

Directions

Read Question 1 and its solution. Then, solve for x in Questions 2 and 3.

1. Solve for x in the triangle shown at the right.

   Step 1 The Triangle Sum Theorem states that the sum of all three angles of a triangle is 180°. Write and solve for x.

   $x + 50 + 45 = 180$.

   Step 2 Solve the equation for x.

   $x + 50 + 45 = 180$

   $x + 95 = 180$

   $x = 85$

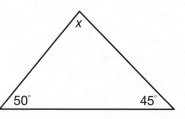

2. 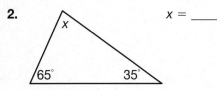 $x = $ _____

3. 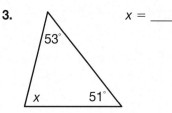 $x = $ _____

Read Question 4 and its solution. Then solve for x in Question 5.

4. Solve for x in the triangle at the right.

   Step 1 The Exterior Angle Sum Theorem states that an exterior angle is equal to the sum of the two nonadjacent interior angles. Write and solve an equation for x.

   $x + 50 = 120$

   Step 2 Solve the equation for x.

   $x = 70$

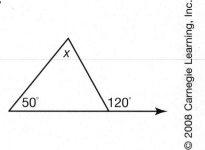

5. $x = $ _____

Origami

Classifying Triangles

Students should be able to answer these questions after Lesson 3.4:

■ How are triangles classified according to their side length?

■ How are triangles classified according to their angle measures?

Directions

Read Question 1 and its solution. Then classify each triangle in Questions 2 through 4 according to its sides and angles.

1. Classify the triangle below according to its sides and angles.

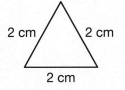

2 cm   2 cm

2 cm

Step 1 The triangle is equilateral because all three sides are equal.

Step 2 The triangle is equiangular because all three angles are equal.

2.

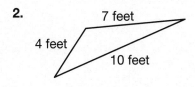

7 feet

4 feet

10 feet

3.

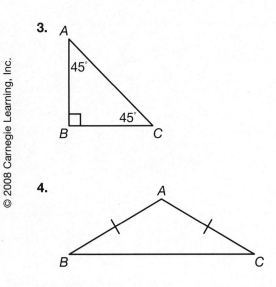

A

45°

45°

B   *C*

4.

A

B   *C*

Building a Shed
The Triangle Inequality

Students should be able to answer these questions after Lesson 3.5:

■ How is the Triangle Inequality used in problem solving?

■ What is the relationship between the angles and sides of a triangle?

Directions

Read Question 1 and its solution. Then find the possible lengths of the third side of each triangle in Questions 2 and 3.

1. What are the possible lengths of the third side of the triangle?

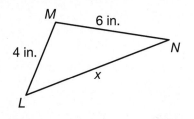

Step 1 The Triangle Inequality Theorem states that the length of one side of a triangle must be less than the sum of the lengths of the other sides of the triangle. The sum of the two known sides is 10, and the difference is 2. So x must be larger than 2 and smaller than 10, or $2 < x < 10$.

2.

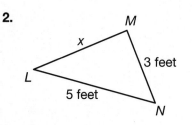

3.

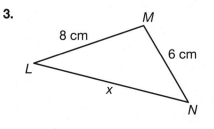

Read Question 4 and its solution. Then list the sides of the triangle in Question 5 in order from least to greatest.

4. List the sides of the triangle in order from least to greatest.

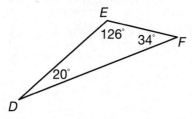

Step 1 The shortest side is opposite the smallest angle. So, $\overline{EF}$ is the shortest side. The longest side is opposite the largest angle. So, $\overline{DF}$ is the longest side.

Step 2 The sides of the triangle in order from least to greatest are $\overline{EF}, \overline{DE}, \overline{DF}$.

5.

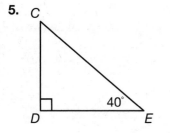

3

Tiling a Bathroom Wall
Simplifying Square Root Expressions

Students should be able to answer these questions after Lesson 4.1:
- How do you simplify square roots?
- How do you simplify a fraction that contains a radical in the denominator?

Read Question 1 and its solution. Then, simplify each expression in Questions 2 through 10.

1. Simplify each expression.

   a. $\sqrt{64}$

   Step 1 The expression $8^2 = 64$. So, $\sqrt{64} = 8$.

   b. $\sqrt{50}$

   Step 1 To simplify, factor out the perfect square 25.
   $$\sqrt{50} = \sqrt{25 \cdot 2} = \sqrt{25} \cdot \sqrt{2} = 5\sqrt{2}$$

   c. $\dfrac{7}{\sqrt{3}}$

   Step 1 Multiply the fraction by the form of 1, $\dfrac{\sqrt{3}}{\sqrt{3}}$. $\dfrac{7}{\sqrt{3}} = \dfrac{7}{\sqrt{3}} \cdot \dfrac{\sqrt{3}}{\sqrt{3}}$

   Step 2 Multiply the numerators and the denominators. $= \dfrac{7 \cdot \sqrt{3}}{\sqrt{3} \cdot \sqrt{3}}$

   Step 3 Write the product as a single square root. $= \dfrac{7\sqrt{3}}{\sqrt{9}}$

   Step 4 Simplify. $= \dfrac{7\sqrt{3}}{3}$

2. $\sqrt{121}$

3. $\sqrt{16} \cdot \sqrt{49}$

4. $\sqrt{27}$

5. $\sqrt{75}$

6. $\sqrt{98}$

7. $\dfrac{1}{\sqrt{6}}$

8. $\dfrac{8}{\sqrt{5}}$

9. $\dfrac{9}{2\sqrt{3}}$

10. $\dfrac{4\sqrt{3}}{\sqrt{2}}$

Installing a Satellite Dish

The Pythagorean Theorem

Students should be able to answer these questions after Lesson 4.2:

- What is the Pythagorean Theorem?
- How do you use the Pythagorean Theorem to find the hypotenuse of a right triangle?

Directions

Read Question 1 and its solution. Then find the missing side lengths to the nearest tenth in Questions 2 through 7.

1. What is the length of the hypotenuse in the triangle shown at the right?

   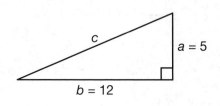

   Step 1 Identify the parts of the right triangle.

   Sides *a* and *b* are the legs, and side *c* is the hypotenuse.

   Step 2 Substitute the known side lengths into the Pythagorean Theorem.

   $$a^2 + b^2 = c^2$$
   $$5^2 + 12^2 = c^2$$

   Step 3 Solve the equation for *c*.

   $$25 + 144 = c^2$$
   $$169 = c^2$$
   $$13 = c$$

   So, the length of the hypotenuse is 13 units.

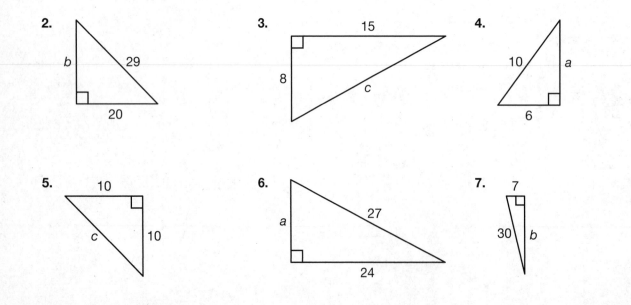

2.

3.

4.

5.

6.

7.

4.3 Drafting Equipment

Properties of 45°-45°-90° Triangles

Students should be able to answer these questions after Lesson 4.3:

- What is the relationship among the side lengths of a 45°-45°-90° triangle?
- Can you find unknown side lengths of a 45°-45°-90° triangle?
- Can you find the area of a 45°-45°-90° triangle?

Directions

Read Question 1 and its solution. Then find the unknown side lengths in Questions 2 through 4.

1. Find the unknown side lengths in the triangle shown at the right. Then find the area of the triangle.

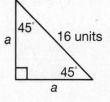

   Step 1 Use the 45°-45°-90° Triangle Theorem.

   Hypotenuse $= \sqrt{2} \cdot$ leg

   Step 2 Substitute the known hypotenuse and solve for a leg.

   $$16 = \sqrt{2} \cdot a$$

   $$\frac{16}{\sqrt{2}} = a$$

   $$\frac{16}{\sqrt{2}} \cdot \frac{\sqrt{2}}{\sqrt{2}} = a$$

   $$\frac{16\sqrt{2}}{2} = a$$

   $$8\sqrt{2} = a$$

   So, the length of each leg is $8\sqrt{2}$ units.

   Step 3 Find the area of the triangle.

   $$\text{Area} = \frac{1}{2}(8\sqrt{2})(8\sqrt{2}) = \frac{1}{2}(64)(\sqrt{4}) = \frac{1}{2}(64)(2) = 64$$

   So, the area of the triangle is 64 square units.

2.

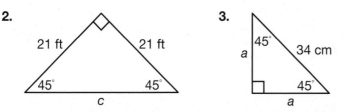

3.

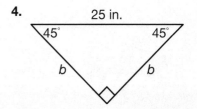

4.

Students should be able to answer these questions after Lesson 4.4:

■ What is the relationship among the side lengths of a 30°-60°-90° triangle?

■ Can you find unknown side lengths of a 30°-60°-90° triangle?

■ Can you find the area of a 30°-60°-90° triangle?

Directions

Read Question 1 and its solution. Then find the unknown side lengths and the area of each triangle in Questions 2 through 4.

1. Find the unknown side lengths in the triangle shown at the right. Then find the area of the triangle.

   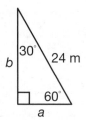

   Step 1 Use the 30°-60°-90° Triangle Theorem.

   Hypotenuse = 2 • shorter leg

   Longer leg = $\sqrt{3}$ • shorter leg

   Step 2 Substitute the known hypotenuse and solve for the shorter leg.

   $24 = 2a$

   $12 = a$

   So, the length of the shorter leg is 12 meters.

   Step 3 Substitute the shorter leg and solve for the longer leg.

   $b = \sqrt{3} \cdot a = \sqrt{3} \cdot 12 = 12\sqrt{3}$

   So, the length of the longer leg is $12\sqrt{3}$ meters.

   Step 4 Find the area.

   $$Area = \frac{1}{2}(12)(12\sqrt{3}) = 72\sqrt{3}$$

   So, the area of the triangle is $72\sqrt{3}$ square units.

2.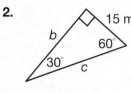

3.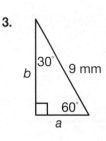

4.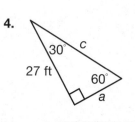

Meeting Friends

The Distance Formula

Students should be able to answer these questions after Lesson 4.5:

■ What is the Distance Formula?

■ How do you find the distance between two points?

Directions

Read Question 1 and its solution. Then complete Questions 2 through 5.

1. Find the distance between the points (–2, –4) and (1, –6) to the nearest tenth.

   Step 1 Identify $x_1, x_2, y_1,$ and y_2.

   $x_1 = -2, x_2 = 1, y_1 = -4, y_2 = -6$

   Step 2 Substitute the known values into the Distance Formula and simplify.

   $$d = \sqrt{(x_2 - x_1)^2 + (y_2 - y_1)^2}$$
   $$= \sqrt{[1 - (-2)]^2 + [-6 - (-4)]^2}$$
   $$= \sqrt{(3)^2 + (-2)^2}$$
   $$= \sqrt{9 + 4}$$
   $$= \sqrt{13} \approx 3.6$$

   So, the distance between the points (–2, –4) and (1, –6) is about 3.6 units.

2. Find the distance between the points (0, 8) and (–5, –9) to the nearest tenth.

3. Find the distance between the points (–4, 2) and (7, 4) to the nearest tenth.

4. Find the distance between the points (6, 6) and (2, –6) to the nearest tenth.

5. The distance between the points (0, –3) and (x, 5) is 10 units. Use the Distance Formula to find the value of x.

Treasure Hunt
The Midpoint Formula

Students should be able to answer these questions after Lesson 4.6:

■ What is the Midpoint Formula?

■ How do you find the midpoint between two endpoints of a line segment?

Directions

Read Question 1 and its solution. Then complete Questions 2 through 5.

1. Find the midpoint of the line segment shown at the right.

   Step 1 Identify x_1, x_2, y_1, and y_2.

   $x_1 = -5$, $x_2 = 4$, $y_1 = 2$, $y_2 = -4$

   Step 2 Substitute the known values into the Midpoint Formula and simplify.

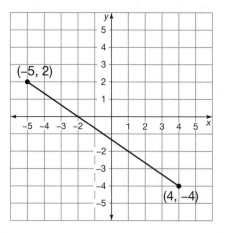

   $$\text{Midpoint} = \left(\frac{x_1 + x_2}{2}, \frac{y_1 + y_2}{2} \right)$$

   $$= \left(\frac{-5 + 4}{2}, \frac{2 + (-4)}{2} \right)$$

   $$= \left(-\frac{1}{2}, -1 \right)$$

   So, the midpoint of the line segment that has endpoints (–5, 2) and (4, –4) is $\left(-\frac{1}{2}, -1 \right)$.

2. Find the midpoint of the line segment that has the endpoints (8, –6) and (–8, –4).

3. Find the midpoint of the line segment that has the endpoints (–3, 9) and (7, 4).

4. Find the midpoint of the line segment that has the endpoints (5, –10) and (–11, –4).

5. The midpoint of the line segment that has the endpoints (–6, x), and (–12, –7) is (–9, 1). Use the Midpoint Formula to find the value of x.

Visiting Washington, D.C.

Transversals and Parallel Lines

Students should be able to answer these questions after Lesson 5.1:

- What is the relationship between the angles formed by two parallel lines and a transversal?
- How are the angles formed by two lines and a transversal classified?

Directions

Read Question 1 and its solution. Then find the measures of the angles in Question 2.

1. Lines ℓ and m are parallel and $m\angle 8 = 45°$. Identify all of the indicated angle pairs and find the measure of each angle.

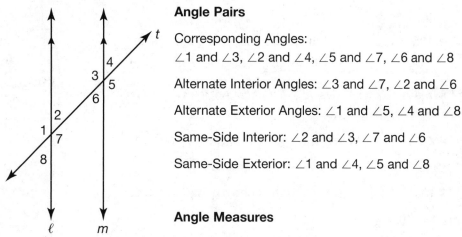

Angle Pairs

Corresponding Angles:
∠1 and ∠3, ∠2 and ∠4, ∠5 and ∠7, ∠6 and ∠8

Alternate Interior Angles: ∠3 and ∠7, ∠2 and ∠6

Alternate Exterior Angles: ∠1 and ∠5, ∠4 and ∠8

Same-Side Interior: ∠2 and ∠3, ∠7 and ∠6

Same-Side Exterior: ∠1 and ∠4, ∠5 and ∠8

Angle Measures

$m\angle 1 = 135°, m\angle 2 = 45°, m\angle 3 = 135°, m\angle 4 = 45°,$
$m\angle 5 = 135°, m\angle 6 = 45°$

2. Lines ℓ and m are parallel and $m\angle 5 = 100°$.

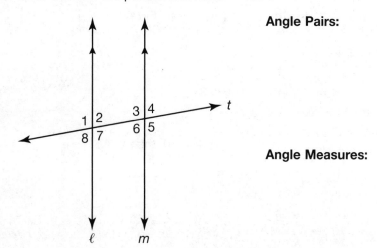

Angle Pairs:

Angle Measures:

© 2008 Carnegie Learning, Inc.

5

Going Up?

Introduction to Proofs

Students should be able to answer these questions after Lesson 5.2:

- How are the hypothesis and conclusion of a conditional statement identified?
- How are geometric properties used in proofs?

Directions

Read Question 1 and its solution. Then complete Question 2.

1. In the figure shown at the right, $m\angle 3 = 105°$. Find the measure of angles 1 and 2.

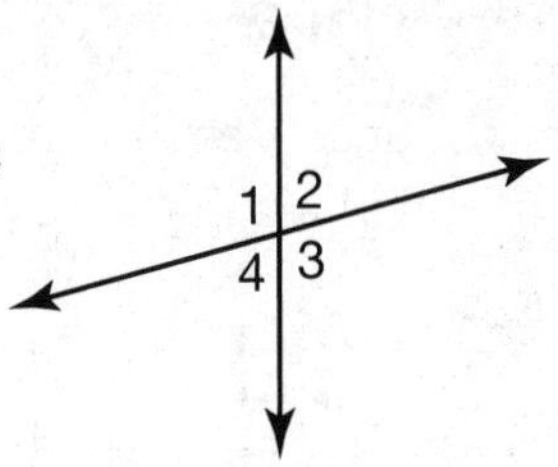

   Step 1 Find the measure of $\angle 2$. Angles 2 and 3 are supplementary because the angles form a linear pair. The sum of the measures of supplementary angles is 180°.

   $m\angle 2 + m\angle 3 = 180°$

   $m\angle 2 + 105° = 180°$ Substitute the known angle measure.

   $m\angle 2 = 75°$ Solve for $m\angle 2$.

   Step 2 Find the measure of $\angle 1$. Using the Vertical Angles Congruence Theorem, $\angle 1$ is congruent to $\angle 3$. So, $m\angle 1 = m\angle 3$.

   $\angle 1 \cong \angle 3$ Vertical Angles Congruence Theorem

   $m\angle 1 = m\angle 3$ Definition of congruence

   $m\angle 1 = 105°$ Substitute the known angle measure.

   So, $m\angle 1 = 105°$ and $m\angle 2 = 75°$.

2. Using the figure shown above, find $m\angle 4$.

Read Question 3 and its solution. Then identify the property in Questions 4 through 6.

3. If $x = 5$, then $5 = x$.

   Reason: Symmetric Property

4. If $x = 2$ and $2 = y$, then $x = y$.

   Reason: _____

5. If $x = 5$, then $x + 2 = 5 + 2$.

   Reason: _____

6. If $x + 4 = 10$, then $x = 6$.

   Reason: _____

Working with Iron
Parallel Lines and Proofs

Students should be able to answer these questions after Lesson 5.3:

■ How are the Alternate Interior and Alternate Exterior Angles Theorems proven?

■ How is the Same-Side Interior Angles Theorem proven?

■ How are geometric properties used in proofs?

Directions

In the diagram below, lines ℓ and m are parallel. Angle 1 measures 60° and angle 2 measures 120°. Find the measure of each angle and explain how you found your answer. Question 1 may be used as an example.

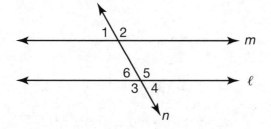

1. $m\angle 3 = 120°$; Sample answer: Angles 2 and 3 are congruent by the Alternate Exterior Angles Postulate

2. $m\angle 4$

3. $m\angle 5$

4. $m\angle 6$

Match the statement in Questions 5 through 9 with the property or definition that justifies it. Question 5 may be used as an example.

__c__ 5. If $x + y = 10$ and $y = 5$, then $x + 5 = 10$.

_____ 6. If $m\angle 1 = m\angle 2$, then $\angle 1 \cong \angle 2$.

_____ 7. In the diagram above, $\angle 3 \cong \angle 5$.

_____ 8. If $x = y$ and $y = z$, then $x = z$.

_____ 9. If $\angle 1$ and $\angle 2$ are supplementary, then $m\angle 1 + m\angle 2 = 180°$.

a. Vertical angles are congruent

b. Definition of congruent angles

c. Substitution Property of Equality

d. Definition of supplementary angles

e. Transitive Property of Equality

5.4 Parking Lot Design

Parallel and Perpendicular Lines in the Coordinate Plane

Students should be able to answer these questions after Lesson 5.4:

■ How are the slopes of parallel and perpendicular lines determined?

■ How are the equations of parallel and perpendicular lines determined?

■ How are the equations of horizontal and vertical lines determined?

Directions

Read Question 1 and its solution. Then, write the equations of one line parallel to and one line perpendicular to the given line in Questions 2 and 3.

1. Write the equation of one line that is parallel and one that is perpendicular to the line represented by the equation $y = 2x + 1$.

   Step 1 Identify the slope of the equation. The slope is the coefficient of the x-term. In this example, the slope is 2.

   Step 2 Determine the slopes of the parallel and perpendicular lines. Parallel lines have the same slope. Lines parallel to $y = 2x + 1$ have a slope of 2. Perpendicular lines have slopes that are negative reciprocals of each other. Lines perpendicular to $y = 2x + 1$ have a slope of $-\dfrac{1}{2}$.

   Step 3 Write the equations of the lines. The value of the constant in the equation does not affect whether the line is parallel or perpendicular.

   Parallel Line: $y = 2x + 7$ Perpendicular Line: $y = -\dfrac{1}{2}x - 4$

2. $y = 3x - 5$

   Parallel Line: _____

   Perpendicular Line: _____

3. $y = -\dfrac{2}{3}x + 1$

   Parallel Line: _____

   Perpendicular Line: _____

Read Question 4 and its solution. Then complete Question 5.

4. Write the equation of a horizontal line and a vertical line that passes through the point (–1, 2).

   Step 1 A horizontal line will pass through the y-coordinate. The horizontal line has the equation $y = 2$.

   Step 2 A vertical line will pass through the x-coordinate. The vertical line has the equation $x = -1$.

5. Write the equation of a horizontal line and a vertical line that passes through (3, –6).

5.5 Building a Henge

Exploring Triangles in the Coordinate Plane

Students should be able to answer these questions after Lesson 5.5:

- How are the coordinates of midsegments determined?
- What are the properties of a midsegment?

Directions

Use the graph shown below to answer the following questions.

The circle on the coordinate plane represents the ditch of a henge. Each grid square represents a square that is four meters long and four meters wide. The three points indicated on the circle represent entrances to the inner area of the henge.

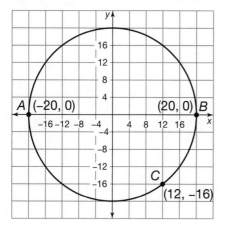

Read Question 1a and its solution. Then complete Questions 1b through 3.

1. Connect the points A, B, and C with line segments. These segments form a right triangle. Find the slope and length of each side.

   a. Slope of $\overline{AB} = \dfrac{y_2 - y_1}{x_2 - x_1} = \dfrac{0 - 0}{20 - (-20)} = \dfrac{0}{40} = 0$

   length of $\overline{AB} = \sqrt{(x_2 - x_1)^2 + (y_2 - y_1)^2} = \sqrt{[20 - (-20)]^2 + (0 - 0)^2} = \sqrt{40^2} = 40$

   b. Slope of $\overline{BC} =$

   length of $\overline{BC} =$

   c. Slope of $\overline{CA} =$

   length of $\overline{CA} =$

2. Find the midpoint of each side of the triangle.

   a. Midpoint of $\overline{AB}$

   b. Midpoint of $\overline{BC}$

   c. Midpoint of $\overline{AC}$

3. Label the midpoint of $\overline{AB}$ as D, label the midpoint of $\overline{BC}$ as E, and label the midpoint of $\overline{AC}$ as F. Draw segments $\overline{DE}$, $\overline{EF}$, and $\overline{DF}$. These segments are called midsegments. Find the slope and the length of each midsegment.

   a. Slope of $\overline{DE}$ =

   length of $\overline{DE}$ =

   b. Slope of $\overline{EF}$ =

   length of $\overline{EF}$ =

   c. Slope of $\overline{DF}$ =

   length of $\overline{DF}$ =

Building a Roof Truss

Angle and Line Segment Bisectors

Students should be able to answer these questions after Lesson 5.6:

■ What are the properties of an angle bisector?

■ What are the properties of a line segment bisector?

Directions

Read Question 1 and its solution. Then complete Questions 2 and 3.

1. If $m\angle A = 35°$, what is the measure of each angle formed when $\angle A$ is bisected?

    Step 1 The measure of each angle is half of $m\angle A$. So, each angle is 17.5°.

2. If $m\angle A = 130°$, what is the measure of each angle formed when $\angle A$ is bisected?

3. What is the measure of $\angle A$ if its bisected angles measure 30°?

Read Question 4 and its solution. Then complete Questions 5 and 6.

4. A line segment that is 30 inches long is bisected. What is the measure of the line segments that are formed by the segment bisector?

    Step 1 The length of each line segment is half of the length of the original segment. So, each segment is 15 inches.

5. A line segment that is 22 inches long is bisected. What is the measure of the line segments that are formed by the segment bisector?

6. If the segments formed by a segment bisector are 13 cm long, what is the original length of the segment that was bisected?

Students should be able to answer these questions after Lesson 5.7:

- How is the incenter of a triangle determined?
- How is the circumcenter of a triangle determined?
- How is the centroid of a triangle determined?
- How is the orthocenter of a triangle determined?
- What are the properties of these points of concurrency?

Directions

Read Question 1 and its solution. Then complete Questions 2 through 4.

1. The **incenter of a triangle** is the point at which the angle bisectors meet. If the distance from the incenter to one side of the triangle is 5 cm, what is the distance from the Incenter to the other sides?

   Step 1   The distance from the incenter to the sides of the triangle are all the same. So, the distance is 5 cm.

2. The **circumcenter** is the point at which the perpendicular bisectors of the triangle meet. If the distance from the circumcenter to one of the vertices is 10 cm, what is the distance from the circumcenter to the other two vertices?

3. The **centroid** is the point at which the medians of a triangle meet. If one median has a distance of 15 mm, what is the distance from its vertex to the centroid?

4. The **orthocenter** is the point at which the altitudes of a triangle intersect. For what type of triangle will the orthocenter be located outside of the triangle? For what type of triangle will it be located on the triangle?

6.1 Paper Snowflakes
Reflections

Students should be able to answer these questions after Lesson 6.1:

- What does it mean for an image to be symmetric?
- How is an image reflected about the *x*- and *y*-axes?
- How are polygons reflected about the line *y* = *x*?

Directions

Read Question 1a and its solution. Then identify whether a horizontal or vertical line of reflection can be drawn through each letter in Questions 1b through 1e.

1. Identify whether a horizontal or vertical line of reflection can be drawn through the indicated letter.

   a. X

   Step 1   A horizontal line of reflection can be placed through the middle of the letter and the exact same image is on the top and bottom—a mirror reflection. A vertical line of reflection can also be drawn so that the same image is on the left and right.

   b. A   c. Y   d. E   e. G

Read Question 2 and its solution. Then identify the coordinates of the point in Questions 3 through 5 when it is reflected about the *x*-axis, *y*-axis, and the line *y* = *x*.

2. Given the point (–2, 3) as a preimage, identify the coordinates of its image after it is reflected about the *x*-axis, the *y*-axis, and the line *y* = *x*.

   Step 1   When (–2, 3) is reflected about the *x*-axis, the point will move down to (–2, –3).

   Step 2   When (–2, 3) is reflected about the *y*-axis, it will move over to (2, 3).

   Step 3   When (–2, 3) is reflected about the line *y* = *x* it moves to (3, –2).

3. (–3, 5)

4. (5, 8)

5. (0, 2)

6

Good Lighting

Rotations

Students should be able to answer these questions after Lesson 6.2:

- What is a rotation?
- How are rotations within the coordinate plane performed?

Directions

Read Question 1 and its solution. The center of rotation is the origin. Then identify the coordinates of each point in Questions 2 and 3 after it has been rotated 90° counterclockwise, 180°, and 90° clockwise.

1. Identify the coordinates of the point below after it has been rotated 90° counterclockwise, 180°, and 90° clockwise.

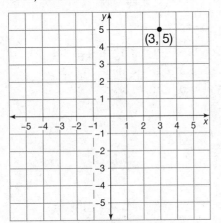

   Step 1   90° counterclockwise: (–5, 3)

   Step 2   180°: (–3, –5)

   Step 3   90° clockwise: (5, –3)

2. (–2, 4)

3. (4, –3)

6

6.3 Web Page Design
Translations

Students should be able to answer these questions after Lesson 6.3:

- How are translations performed using the coordinate system?
- What is the relationship between reflections and translations?

Directions

Read Question 1 and its solution. Then complete Question 2.

1. A rectangle with vertices (–2, 3), (–2, 8), (5, 3), and (5, 8) is shifted vertically by 4 units. Find the coordinates of the new image.

   Step 1 Because the image is shifted vertically, the *y*-coordinate will change by by 4 units. The *x*-coordinate will not change.

   The coordinates become: $(-2, 3 + 4)$, $(-2, 8 + 4)$, $(5, 3 + 4)$, $(5, 8 + 4) = (-2, 7), (-2, 12), (5, 7), (5, 12)$.

2. A triangle with vertices (–3, 0), (0, 5), and (4, 0) is shifted horizontally 7 units. Find the coordinates of the new image.

Read Question 3 and its solution. Then complete Question 4.

3. The vertices of a square are $A(-5, 0)$, $B(5, 0)$, $C(-5, 4)$, and $D(5, 4)$. This square is transformed by using the translation $(x, y) \rightarrow (x + 1, y - 2)$. Describe the movement of the preimage that will create the image. Use a complete sentence in your answer.

   Step 1 The square will be shifted horizontally to the right 1 unit, and vertically down by 2 units.

4. The vertices of a triangle are $A(1, 2)$, $B(-2, 5)$, and $C(0, -7)$, This triangle is transformed by using the translation $(x, y) \rightarrow (x - 2, y + 3)$. Describe the movement of the preimage that will create the image, and provide the coordinates of the image's vertices. Use complete sentences in your answer.

6

Shadow Puppets
Dilations

Students should be able to answer these questions after Lesson 6.4:
- How is the scale factor of a dilation determined?
- How are dilations performed in the coordinate plane using coordinate notation?

Directions

Read Question 1 and its solution. Then complete Question 2.

1. A triangle with vertices (–4, 0), (0, 8), and (6, 0) is dilated by a factor of 3. Determine if the dilated image will be larger or smaller. Find the coordinates of the new image.

   Step 1 The triangle will be larger because the scale factor is greater than 1. (If the scale factor were between 0 and 1, the triangle would be smaller.)

   Step 2 The coordinates of the triangle will triple. The new coordinates will be (–12, 0), (0, 24), and (18, 0).

2. A rectangle with vertices (–2, –1), (5, –1), (–2, 4), and (5, 4) is dilated by a scale factor of 0.5. Determine whether the dilated image will be larger or smaller. Find the coordinates of the new image.

Read Question 3 and its solution. Then complete Question 4.

3. The dimensions of a preimage and its dilated image are given. Find the scale factor.

Preimage	Dilated Image
$AB = 10$	$AD = 5$
$AC = 20$	$AE = 10$
$BC = 15$	$DE = 7.5$

   Step 1 Find the ratio of the lengths of the dilated image to the preimage.

   $\frac{5}{10} = \frac{10}{20} = \frac{7.5}{15} = \frac{1}{2}$. So, the scale factor is $\frac{1}{2}$, or 0.5.

4. The length of one side of a dilated square was transformed from 5 feet to 2 feet. Find the scale factor.

6

Cookie Cutters

Symmetry

Students should be able to answer these questions after Lesson 6.5:

- How are symmetry lines determined?
- How is rotational symmetry determined?

Directions

Read Question 1 and its solution. Then identify the number of lines of symmetry that exist for each figure in Questions 2 and 3.

1. How many lines of symmetry does the figure have?

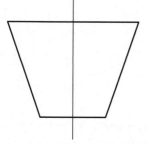

Step 1   A line of symmetry is a line that divides the figure into identical parts. Each side of the symmetry line is a mirror image of the other. In this instance, a vertical line is the only line of symmetry.

2.

3.

6

Read Question 4 and its solution. Then determine whether each figure in Questions 5 and 6 has rotational symmetry.

4. A plane figure has rotational symmetry if you can rotate the figure less than or equal to 180° and the resulting figure is the same as the original figure in the same position.

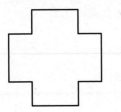

Step 1 The figure does have rotational symmetry. A 90° turn results in the exact same image.

5.

6.

6

7.1 Ace Reporter

Ratio and Proportion

Students should be able to answer these questions after Lesson 7.1:

- How are ratios written and used to solve problems?
- How are ratios used in surveys to make predictions?

Directions

Read Question 1 and its solution. Then complete Questions 2 and 3.

The table below shows the ice cream preference of students in the class.

What flavor of ice cream do you prefer?		
Vanilla	**Chocolate**	**Strawberry**
8	10	6

1. What is the ratio of students who prefer vanilla to the total number of students surveyed?

   Step 1 A ratio is a comparison of two numbers written as a fraction. In this survey, 8 students preferred vanilla out of 24 total students (8 + 10 + 6). So, the ratio of students who prefer vanilla to the total number of students surveyed is $\frac{8}{24}$ or $\frac{1}{3}$.

2. What is the ratio of students who prefer chocolate to students who prefer strawberry?

3. What is the ratio of students who prefer chocolate to the total number of students?

Read Question 4 and its solution. Then complete Question 5.

4. Using the results of the survey above, if 100 students were surveyed, about how many would you expect to prefer strawberry ice cream?

   Step 1 Six out of 24 students prefer strawberry. A proportion to find the number of students out of 100 who prefer strawberry is $\frac{6}{24} = \frac{x}{100}$. Reduce the fraction to get $\frac{1}{4} = \frac{x}{100}$.

   Step 2 Because (4)(25) = 100, multiply 1 by 25 to find that 25 students prefer strawberry.

5. If 200 students were surveyed, estimate the number of students who would prefer vanilla.

Framing a Picture

Similar and Congruent Polygons

7

Students should be able to answer these questions after Lesson 7.2:

■ How are similar and congruent polygons identified?

■ How are ratios used in determining unknown sides of similar figures?

Directions

Read Question 1 and its solution. Then solve for *x* in Questions 2 and 3.

1. △*ABC* ~ △*DEF*

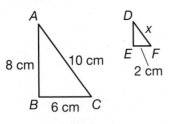

Step 1 Corresponding sides of similar triangles are proportional. Write a proportion that that can be used to solve for *x*.

$$\frac{10}{x} = \frac{6}{2}$$

Step 2 Solve the proportion by cross-multiplying and dividing.

$$6x = 20$$

$$x = \frac{20}{6} = 3.\overline{3} \text{ cm}$$

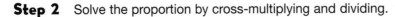

2. △*ABC* ~ △*DEF*

3. △*ABC* ~ △*DEF*

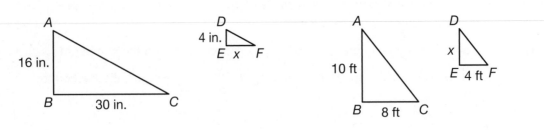

Read Question 4 and its solution. Then complete Question 5.

4. A student is painting a picture of a house. The actual house is 22 feet tall, while the painting of the house is 2 feet tall. What is the scale factor of the painting?

   Step 1   The scale factor is the ratio of the painting to the actual house.

   The scale factor of the painting is $\dfrac{2\text{ ft}}{22\text{ ft}}$ or $\dfrac{1\text{ ft}}{11\text{ ft}}$.

5. The porch of the house described in Question 4 is 16.5 feet wide. In the painting of the house, the width of the porch is 1.5 feet. Did the painter use the correct proportion? Why or why not? Use complete sentences in your answer.

Using an Art Projector

Proving Triangles Similar: AA, SSS, SAS

7

Students should be able to answer these questions after Lesson 7.3:

■ How can you prove that two triangles are similar?

■ How is a similarity statement written?

Directions

Read Question 1 and its solution. Then decide whether the triangles in Questions 2 and 3 are similar. If they are similar, write a similarity statement.

Using the similarity rules, decide whether the triangles are similar. If they are similar, write a similarity statement.

1.

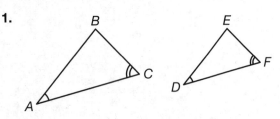

Step I   *ABC ~ DEF* because of the AA Similarity Theorem. Two of the angles are congruent, so the triangles must be similar.

In the similarity statement, the vertices of the congruent angles correspond to each other.

2.

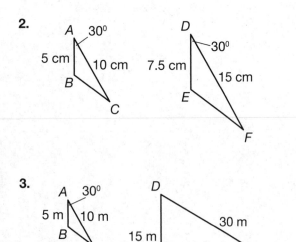

3.

Modeling a Park

Indirect Measurement

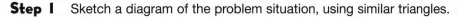

Students should be able to answer this question after Lesson 7.4:

■ How can the height and width of objects be determined indirectly?

Directions

Read Question 1 and its solution. Then complete Question 2.

1. On a sunny day a class goes outside to conduct an experiment to see how tall the school is. Alicia is 65 inches tall and casts a shadow that is 30 inches long. She and her partner measure the shadow cast by the school building and find that it is approximately 20 feet long. Approximately how tall is the school building?

   Step 1 Sketch a diagram of the problem situation, using similar triangles.

   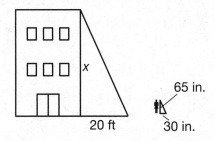

   65 in.

   20 ft   30 in.

   Step 2 Make any necessary unit conversions. In this problem, convert feet to inches.

   $$\frac{20 \text{ ft}}{1} \times \frac{12 \text{ in.}}{1 \text{ ft}} = 240 \text{ in.}$$

   Step 3 Set up a proportion using similar triangles and solve for x.

   $$\frac{x}{65} = \frac{20}{30}$$

   $$30x = 1300$$

   $$x = 43.3$$

   So, the school building is approximately 43 feet tall.

2. A committee from the Parks and Recreation planning group has submitted an idea for a triangular dog park. On paper, the length of the dog park along the river is 10 inches and the length along the tree line is 15 inches. If the actual length along the tree line is 120 feet, what is the actual length along the river?

Making Plastic Containers

Similar Solids

7

Students should be able to answer these questions after Lesson 7.5:

- How do the volume and surface area of similar solids compare to each other?
- How can you find the dimensions of a similar solid given the scale factor?

Directions

Read Question 1 and its solution. Then write ratios comparing the lengths, surface areas, and volumes for each pair of objects in Questions 2 and 3.

1. **a.** Write a ratio comparing the length of the two cubes below.

   b. Find the ratio of the surface area of the first cube to the surface area of the second cube.

   c. Find the ratio of the volume of the first cube to the volume of the second cube.

   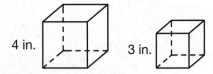

   Solution

   a. The ratio of the two lengths is $\dfrac{4}{3}$.

   b. The surface area is the sum of the area of all surfaces. The first cube has a surface area of (4)(4)(6 sides) = 96 square units. The second cube has a surface area of

   (3)(3)(6 sides) = 54 square units. The ratio of the two surface areas is $\dfrac{96}{54} = \dfrac{16}{9}$.

   c. The volume of the cubes are (4)(4)(4) = 64 cubic units and (3)(3)(3) = 27.

   The ratio of the two volumes is $\dfrac{64}{27}$.

2.

3.

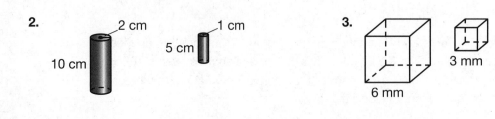

8.1 Glass Lanterns

Introduction to Congruence

Students should be able to answer these questions after Lesson 8.1:

- How are corresponding sides and angles identified in congruent figures?
- What is the relationship between similarity and congruence?
- How can you determine if two polygons are congruent?

Directions

Read Question 1 and its solution. Then complete Questions 2 through 4.

1. In the figure shown below, $\triangle ABC \cong \triangle DEF$. Name each pair of congruent angles and each pair of congruent sides.

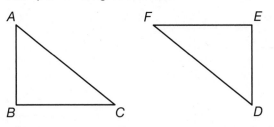

Step 1 Corresponding angles of congruent triangles are congruent. In the congruence statement, the vertices of the congruent angles correspond to each other.

$\angle A$ and $\angle D$, $\angle B$ and $\angle E$, $\angle C$ and $\angle F$

Step 2 Corresponding sides of congruent triangles are equal.

$\overline{AB}$ and $\overline{DE}$, $\overline{AC}$ and $\overline{DF}$, $\overline{BC}$ and $\overline{EF}$

2. Given that $\triangle GHI \cong \triangle JKL$, name each pair of congruent sides and each pair of congruent angles without using a diagram.

3. How are congruent triangles alike? How are they different? Use complete sentences in your answer.

4. How are similar triangles alike? How are they different? Use complete sentences in your answer.

Read Question 5 and its solution. Then complete Question 6.

5. Suppose that $\triangle ABC \cong \triangle DEF$ with $m\angle A = 60°$ and $m\angle B = 90°$. Find the measure of all missing angles.

   Step 1 The sum of the measures of the angles in a triangle is 180°, so $m\angle C = 30°$.

   Step 2 Because the triangles are congruent, corresponding angles are equal.

   $m\angle A = m\angle D, m\angle B = m\angle E, m\angle C = m\angle F$

   So, $m\angle D = 60°$, $m\angle E = 90°$, and $m\angle F = 30°$.

6. Suppose that $\triangle ABC \cong \triangle XYZ$ with $m\angle A = 70°$ and $m\angle B = 50°$. Find the measure of all missing angles.

Computer Graphics

Proving Triangles Congruent: SSS and SAS

Students should be able to answer these questions after Lesson 8.2:

■ How is the SSS Congruence Theorem used to prove that triangles are congruent?

■ How is the SAS Congruence Theorem used to prove that triangles are congruent?

Directions

Read Question 1 and its solution. Then complete Question 2.

1. In the figure shown below, $\overline{GH} \cong \overline{HI}$ and $\overline{KH} \cong \overline{HJ}$. Write a paragraph to prove that $\triangle GHK \cong \triangle IHJ$.

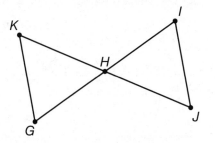

Step 1 Use the SAS Congruence Theorem. Two pairs of corresponding side are given as congruent. Vertical angles are congruent so $\angle KHG \cong \angle JHI$. By SAS, $\triangle GHK \cong \triangle IHJ$.

2. In the figure shown below, $\overline{LM} \cong \overline{PO}$ and N is the midpoint of $\overline{MP}$ and $\overline{LO}$. Write a paragraph to prove $\triangle LNM \cong \triangle ONP$.

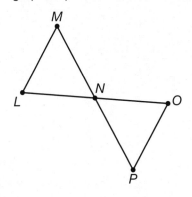

Read Question 3 and its solution. Then complete Question 4.

3. In the figure shown below, $\overline{QR} \cong \overline{QT}$. Can the SSS or SAS Congruence Theorems be used to prove that $\triangle QRS \cong \triangle QTS$? Explain your reasoning.

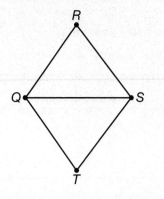

Step 1 You don't have enough information to tell whether the triangles are congruent. You know that $\overline{QR} = \overline{QT}$ and that they share $\overline{QS}$, but you don't have any information about the other side or angles.

4. In the figure shown below $m\angle V = m\angle X$, $\overline{VJ} \cong \overline{JX}$, and $\overline{UJ} \cong \overline{JW}$. Can the SSS or SAS Congruence Theorems be used to prove that $\triangle VJU \cong \triangle XJW$? Explain your reasoning.

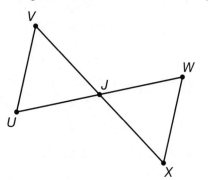

Wind Triangles

Proving Triangles Congruent: ASA and AAS

Students should be able to answer these questions after Lesson 8.3:

- How is the ASA Congruence Theorem used to prove that triangles are congruent?
- How is the AAS Congruence Theorem used to prove that triangles are congruent?

Directions

Read Question 1 and its solution. Then complete Question 2.

1. In the figure shown below $\angle K \cong \angle J$ and $\overline{KH} \cong \overline{HJ}$. Write a paragraph to prove that $\triangle GHK \cong \triangle IHJ$.

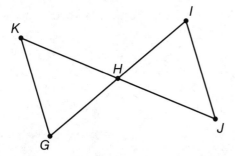

Step 1 Use the ASA Congruence Theorem. Vertical angles are congruent so $\angle KHG \cong \angle JHI$. So, $\triangle GHK \cong \triangle IHJ$ by ASA.

2. In the figure shown below $\angle DCA \cong \angle CAB$ and $\angle DAC \cong \angle BCA$. Write a paragraph to prove that $\triangle CBA \cong \triangle ADC$.

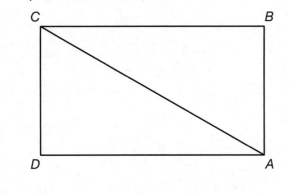

3. In the figure shown below, $m\angle E = m\angle C$, $m\angle A = m\angle D$, and $\overline{EB} = \overline{CD}$. Can the AAS or ASA Congruence Theorems be used to prove that $\triangle BEA \cong \triangle BCD$?

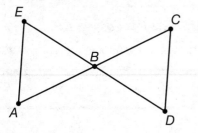

8

Step 1   You don't have enough information to tell whether the triangles are congruent. You know that two pairs of corresponding angles and one pair of corresponding sides are congruent, but they are not in the proper order to use ASA or AAS.

4. In the figure shown below $m\angle F = m\angle H$ and $\overline{JI} \cong \overline{IG}$. Can the AAS or ASA Congruence Theorems be used to prove that $\triangle IFJ \cong \triangle IHG$?

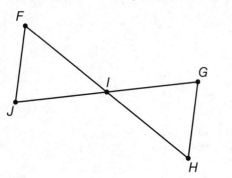

Planting Grape Vines

Proving Triangles Congruent: HL

Students should be able to answer this question after Lesson 8.4:

■ How is the Hypotenuse-Leg Congruence Theorem used to prove that right triangles are congruent?

Directions

Read Question 1 and its solution. Then complete Question 2.

1. In the figure shown below, $m\angle B = m\angle D = 90°$ and E is the midpoint of $\overline{BD}$ and $\overline{AC}$. Name two congruence theorems that could be used to prove $\triangle ABE \cong \triangle CDE$.

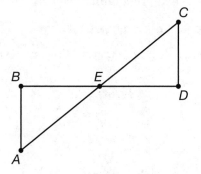

Step 1   The Hypotenuse-Leg Congruence Theorem could be used. Both triangles are right triangles because they each contain a right angle. Point E is the midpoint of $\overline{BD}$ and $\overline{AC}$, so $\overline{BE} \cong \overline{ED}$ and $\overline{AE} = \overline{EC}$. Therefore, $\triangle ABE \cong \triangle CDE$ by HL.

Step 2   The SAS Congruence Theorem could also be used. Point E is the midpoint of $\overline{BD}$ and $\overline{AC}$, so $\overline{BE} \cong \overline{ED}$ and $\overline{AE} \cong \overline{EC}$. Vertical angles are congruent so $\angle AED \cong \angle DEC$. Therefore, $\triangle ABE \cong \triangle CDE$ by SAS.

2. In the figure shown below, $m\angle C = m\angle A = 90°$, $\overline{CB} \cong \overline{AD}$, and $\overline{CB} \parallel \overline{AD}$. Name two congruence theorems that could be used to prove $\triangle CBD \cong \triangle ADB$.

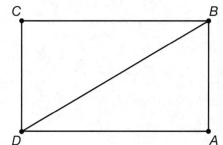

Koch Snowflake

Fractals

Students should be able to answer these questions after Lesson 8.5:

■ What are the properties of fractals?

■ How is a fractal constructed?

Directions

8

Read Question 1 and its solution. Then complete Questions 2 through 5.

1. The creation of the Koch Fractal is shown below. Begin with an equilateral triangle. A new triangle with side lengths that are $\frac{1}{3}$ of the original are added to each side of the original triangle. The third shape in the diagram below results when equilateral triangles that are $\frac{1}{3}$ the length of the previous "new" triangles are added on. The pattern continues in this manner.

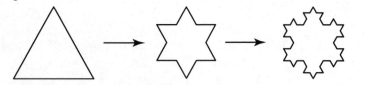

What happens to the total number of sides as the stages of the fractal increase?

Step 1   The total number of sides increases by a multiple of 4 as the stages increase. The first figure has 3 sides. The second figure has 12 sides. The third figure has 48 sides.

2. What happens to the total area as the stages of the fractal increase?

3. What happens to the area of each new triangle as the stages of the fractal increase?

4. What happens to the side length as the stages of the fractal increase?

5. What happens to the perimeter of the figure as the stages of the fractal increase?

9.1 Quilting and Tessellations
Introduction to Quadrilaterals

Students should be able to answer these questions after Lesson 9.1:

■ How are quadrilaterals named?

■ What is the relationship between various quadrilaterals?

Directions

**Use the Venn diagram to answer the following questions as true or false.
Question 1 may be used as an example.**

1. All squares are parallelograms.

   Step 1 True. In the Venn Diagram, the Parallelogram region encompasses all squares, rectangles and rhombi.

2. Some trapezoids may be squares. _____

3. All rectangles are squares._____

4. All squares are rectangles._____

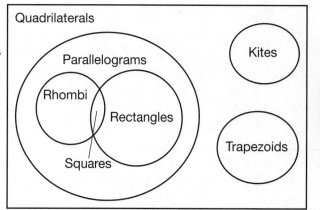

Match each of the figures below with the most specific label.

5. Rhombus _____

6. Rectangle _____

7. Trapezoid _____

8. Kite _____

9. Square _____

10. Parallelogram _____

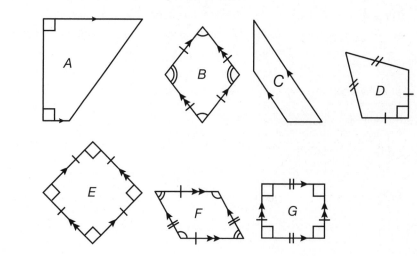

© 2008 Carnegie Learning, Inc.

When Trapezoids Are Kites

Kites and Trapezoids

Students should be able to answer these questions after Lesson 9.2:

- How are complementary and supplementary angles identified?
- How are adjacent angles and vertical angles identified?

Directions

Read Question 1 and its solution. Then complete Questions 2 and 3.

1. Write a paragraph to prove that $\angle A$ is congruent to $\angle C$.

   Step 1 From the diagram, $\overline{BA} \cong \overline{BC}$ and $\overline{AD} \cong \overline{DC}$. By the Reflexive Property, $\overline{BD} \cong \overline{BD}$. So, $\triangle BAD \cong \triangle BCD$ by SSS. Because corresponding parts of congruent triangles are congruent, $\angle BAD \cong \angle BCD$.

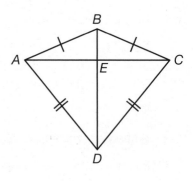

2. What is the measure of $\angle BEA$? Explain your reasoning.

3. What is the relationship between $\overline{AE}$ and segment $\overline{EC}$? Explain your reasoning.

Read Question 4 and its solution. Then complete Question 5.

4. What is the relationship between $m\angle K$ and $m\angle N$? Explain your reasoning.

   Step 1 By using the Hypotenuse-Leg Congruence Theorem, $\triangle MQN \cong \triangle LPK$. Because corresponding parts of congruent triangles are congruent, $m\angle K = m\angle N$.

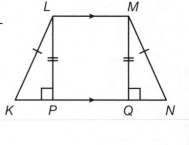

5. What is the relationship between diagonal *KM* and diagonal *LN*? Explain your reasoning.

9.3 Binocular Stand Design

Parallelograms and Rhombi

Students should be able to answer these questions after Lesson 9.3:

- What are the properties of parallelograms?
- What are the properties of rhombi?

Directions

Read Question 1 and its solution. Then complete Question 2.

1. If $m\angle Q = 75°$, find the measures of $\angle S$ and $\angle P$.

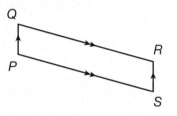

Step 1 Opposite angles of a parallelogram are congruent, so $m\angle S = 75°$.

Step 2 The sum of the measures of consecutive angles of a parallelogram is 180°, so $m\angle P = 180 - 75 = 105°$.

2. If $m\angle P = 100°$, find the measures of $\angle Q$ and $\angle R$.

Read Question 3 and its solution. Then complete Question 4.

3. If $BC = 10$ centimeters and $m\angle C = 80°$, find $AB, m\angle B$, and $m\angle BCA$.

Step 1 All sides of a rhombus are equal, so $AB = 10$ centimeters.

Step 2 The sum of the measures of consecutive angles of a rhombus is 180°, so $m\angle B = 100°$.

Step 3 The diagonals of a rhombus bisect the angles, so $m\angle BCA = 40°$.

4. If $BC = 4$ centimeters and $m\angle D = 120°$, find $AB, m\angle B$, and $m\angle BAC$.

Positive Reinforcement
Rectangles and Squares

Students should be able to answer these questions after Lesson 9.4:

- What are the properties of rectangles?
- What are the properties of squares?

Directions

Read Question 1 and its solution. Then complete Question 2.

1. In the rectangle below, find the length of diagonal *BD* and diagonal *AC*.

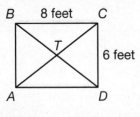

Step 1 The Pythagorean Theorem can be used to find *BD*.

$$6^2 + 8^2 = BD^2$$

$$36 + 64 = BD^2$$

$$100 = BD^2$$

$$\sqrt{100} = 10 = BD$$

Step 2 Diagonals of a rectangle are congruent, so $BD = AC = 10$.

2. If $BC = 7$ meters and $CD = 4$ meters, find *BA*, *AD*, and *BD*.

Read Question 3 and its solution. Then, complete Questions 4 through 6.

3. True or False: The diagonals of a square are perpendicular.

Step 1 True. A 90° angle is formed at the intersection of the diagonals.

4. True or False: All properties of parallelograms apply to squares.

5. True or False: Every rectangle is a square.

6. True or False: Every square is a rectangle.

9.5 Stained Glass
Sum of the Interior Angle Measures in a Polygon

Students should be able to answer these questions after Lesson 9.5:

- How do you determine the sum of the interior angles of a regular polygon?
- How do you determine the measure of each interior angle of a regular polygon?
- Given the measure of each interior angle, how do you determine the number of sides?

Directions

Read Question 1 and its solution. Then complete Question 2.

1. What is the sum of the measures of the interior angles of a regular nonagon?

   Step 1 Use the formula $(n - 2) \cdot 180$, where n is the number of sides. A nonagon has nine sides.

   $(9 - 2) \cdot 180 = 7 \cdot 180 = 1260$

   The sum of the measures of the interior angles of a regular nonagon is 1260°.

2. What is the sum of the measures of the interior angles of a regular dodecagon (12-sided polygon)?

Read Question 3 and its solution. Then complete Questions 4 and 5.

3. What is the measure of each interior angle of a regular nonagon?

   Step 1 Find the sum of the measures of the interior angles of a regular nonagon.

   $(n - 2) \cdot 180 = (9 - 2) \cdot 180 = 1260$

   Step 2 In a regular polygon, all interior angles are congruent. Divide the sum of the measure, of the interior angles by the number of sides.

   The measure of each interior angle of a regular nonagon is 140°.

4. What is the measure of each interior angle of a regular dodecagon (12-sided polygon)?

5. If the measure of each interior angle of a regular polygon is 135°, how many sides does the polygon have? *Hint:* Solve the equation $\dfrac{(n - 2) \cdot 180}{n} = 135$.

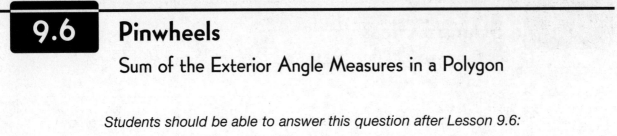

9.6 Pinwheels

Sum of the Exterior Angle Measures in a Polygon

Students should be able to answer this question after Lesson 9.6:

- How do you determine the sum of the exterior angles of a regular polygon using only one exterior angle at each vertex?

Directions

Read Question 1 and its solution. Then complete Questions 2 through 4.

1. What is the sum of the measures of the exterior angles of a regular pentagon?

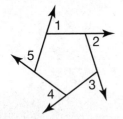

$m\angle 1 + m\angle 2 + m\angle 3 + m\angle 4 + m\angle 5 =$ _____

Step 1 You can see from the diagram that exterior angles are formed when the side of a polygon is extended at a vertex.

Step 2 The sum of the measures of the exterior angles of a regular pentagon is 360°.

2. What is the sum of the measures of the exterior angles of a regular dodecagon?

3. What is the sum of the measures of the exterior angles of a regular octagon?

4. What is the sum of the measures of the interior angles of a pentagon?

Planning a Subdivision

Rectangles and Parallelograms in the Coordinate Plane

Students should be able to answer these questions after Lesson 9.7:

■ How can quadrilaterals in the coordinate plane be classified?

■ How are properties of quadrilaterals in a coordinate plane determined?

Directions

Read Question 1 and its solution. Then complete Questions 2 and 3.

1. What type of quadrilateral is shown below?

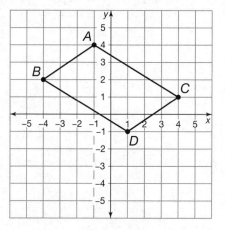

Step 1 Use the slopes of the lines to decide whether the opposite sides are parallel. If opposite sides have the same slope, then they are parallel. The vertices of the quadrilateral are $A(-1, 4)$, $B(-4, 2)$, $C(4, 1)$, and $D(1, -1)$.

Slope of $\overline{AB} = \dfrac{4 - 2}{-1 - (-4)} = \dfrac{2}{3}$ Slope of $\overline{CD} = \dfrac{1 - (-1)}{4 - 1} = \dfrac{2}{3}$

Slope of $\overline{AC} = \dfrac{4 - 1}{-1 - 4} = \dfrac{3}{-5}$ Slope of $\overline{BD} = \dfrac{2 - (-1)}{-4 - 1} = \dfrac{3}{-5}$

Opposite sides have the same slope, so they are parallel. Therefore, the figure is a parallelogram.

Step 2 Use the slopes of the lines to decide whether the adjacent sides are perpendicular. If adjacent sides have negative reciprocal slopes, then they are perpendicular. The adjacent sides are not perpendicular.

Step 3 In the quadrilateral, opposite sides are parallel and adjacent sides are not perpendicular. Therefore, the quadrilateral is a parallelogram.

2. A quadrilateral has vertices (4, 0), (8, 0), (4, 4), and (8, 4). What type of quadrilateral is it?

3. A quadrilateral has vertices (3, 3), (5, 1), (7, 3), and (5, 5). What type of quadrilateral is it?

10.1 Riding a Ferris Wheel

Introduction to Circles

Students should be able to answer these questions after Lesson 10.1:

- What are the parts of a circle?
- How are the parts of a circle drawn?

Directions

Read Question 1 and its solution. Then draw an example of each vocabulary term in Question 2.

1. Identify the following in the circle below:

   - center: O
   - radius: $\overline{OC}$
   - chord: $\overline{CA}$
   - secant: $\overleftrightarrow{GF}$
   - point of tangency: C
   - central angle: $\angle COB$
   - inscribed angle: $\angle CDB$
   - arc: $\overparen{BA}$
   - minor arc: $\overparen{GF}$
   - major arc: $\overparen{GFB}$

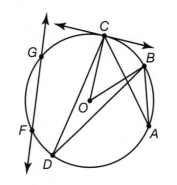

2. Using the circle below, draw and properly label an example of each of the following.

   - center
   - radius
   - chord
   - diameter
   - secant
   - tangent
   - point of tangency
   - central angle
   - inscribed angle
   - arc
   - semicircle
   - minor arc
   - major arc

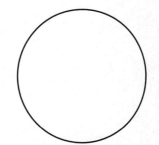

10

Holding the Wheel

Central Angles, Inscribed Angles, and Intercepted Arcs

Students should be able to answer these questions after Lesson 10.2:

- How is the measure of an arc determined?
- How is the measure of an inscribed angle determined?
- How is the measure of a central angle determined?

Directions

Read Question 1 and its solution. Then complete Questions 2 and 3.

1. $m\angle BJA = 50°$

   $m\overarc{BA} = $ _____ °

   $m\angle BCA = $ _____ °

   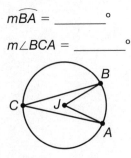

   Step 1 The measure of an intercepted arc is equal to the measure of the central angle, so $m\overarc{BA} = 50°$.

   Step 2 The measure of an inscribed angle is half the measure of the intercepted arc, so $m\angle BCA = 25°$.

2. $m\overarc{MJ} = 70°$

   $m\angle MKJ = $ _____ °

   $m\angle MLJ = $ _____ °

   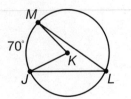

3. $m\angle RIH = 45°$

   $m\overarc{RH} = $ _____ °

   $m\angle RMH = $ _____ °

Students should be able to answer these questions after Lesson 10.3:

■ How is the measure of an angle formed by two chords determined?

■ How is the measure of an angle formed by two secants determined?

■ How is the measure of an angle formed by a secant and a tangent determined?

■ How is the measure of an angle formed by two tangents determined?

Directions

Read Question 1 through 4 and their solutions. Then complete Questions 5 through 8.

1.
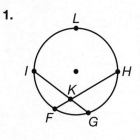

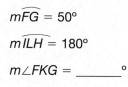

$$m\overarc{FG} = 50°$$

$$m\overarc{ILH} = 180°$$

$$m\angle FKG = \underline{\hspace{1cm}}°$$

Step I $\quad m\angle FKG = \dfrac{180 + 50}{2} = 115°$

2.
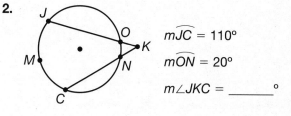

$$m\overarc{JC} = 110°$$

$$m\overarc{ON} = 20°$$

$$m\angle JKC = \underline{\hspace{1cm}}°$$

Step I $\quad m\angle JKC = \dfrac{110 - 20}{2} = 45°$

3.
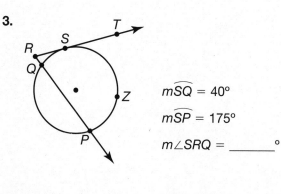

$$m\overarc{SQ} = 40°$$

$$m\overarc{SP} = 175°$$

$$m\angle SRQ = \underline{\hspace{1cm}}°$$

Step I $\quad m\angle SRQ = \dfrac{175 - 40}{2} = 67.5°$

4.
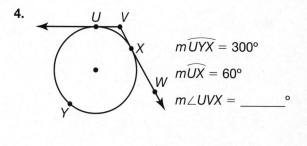

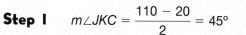

$$m\overarc{UYX} = 300°$$

$$m\overarc{UX} = 60°$$

$$m\angle UVX = \underline{\hspace{1cm}}°$$

Step I $\quad m\angle UVX = \dfrac{300 - 60}{2} = 120°$

10

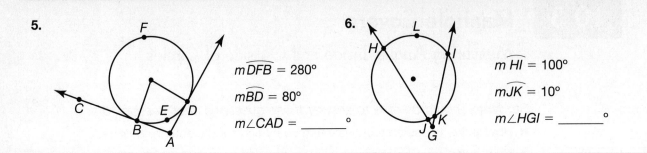

5.

$m\overset{\frown}{DFB} = 280°$

$m\overset{\frown}{BD} = 80°$

$m\angle CAD = $ _____ °

6.

$m\overset{\frown}{HI} = 100°$

$m\overset{\frown}{JK} = 10°$

$m\angle HGI = $ _____ °

7.

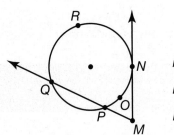

$m\overset{\frown}{PN} = 70°$

$m\overset{\frown}{QRN} = 200°$

$m\angle PMN = $ _____ °

8.

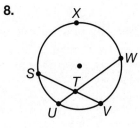

$m\overset{\frown}{UV} = 60°$

$m\overset{\frown}{SXW} = 180°$

$m\angle STW = $ _____ °

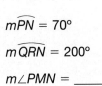

Color Theory
Chords and Circles

Students should be able to answer these questions after Lesson 10.4:

- What is the relationship between the chord and the diameter of a circle?
- What is the relationship between congruent chords and their minor arcs?

Directions

Read Question 1 and its solution. Then complete Questions 2 and 3.

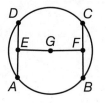

1. **a.** If $\overline{DA} \cong \overline{CB}$, what conclusions can be drawn about the arcs of the circle above?

    Step 1   If two chords in a circle are congruent, then their corresponding minor arcs are congruent. If $\overline{DA} \cong \overline{CB}$, then you know that $\overset{\frown}{DA} \cong \overset{\frown}{CB}$.

    b. If $\overline{GE} \perp \overline{DA}$ and G is the center of the circle, what conclusions can be drawn from the circle above?

    Step 1   If a diameter of a circle is perpendicular to a chord, then the diameter bisects the chord and its arc. If you know that $\overline{GE} \perp \overline{DA}$, you can also conclude that $\overline{DE} \cong \overline{EA}$.

2. In the circle shown at the right, $m\overset{\frown}{DA} = 80°$ and $\overline{DA} \cong \overline{CB}$. Find $m\overset{\frown}{CB}$.

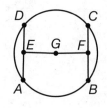

3. In the circle shown at the right, $\overline{DE} \cong \overline{EB}$ and A is the center of the circle.
    Is $\triangle AED \cong \triangle AEB$? Use complete sentences in your answer.

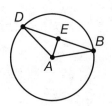

Solar Eclipses

Tangents and Circles

Students should be able to answer these questions after Lesson 10.5:

- What is the relationship between a tangent line and a radius?
- What is the relationship between congruent tangent segments?

Directions

Read Question 1 and its solution. Then complete Questions 2 and 3.

1. In the figure shown below, $JF = 10$ centimeters. Find FG, $m\angle HJF$, and $m\angle HGF$.

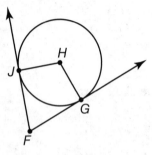

Step 1 If two tangent segments to a circle are drawn from the same point outside the circle, then the tangent segments are congruent. $FG = 10$ centimeters.

Step 2 A tangent to a circle is perpendicular to the radius that is drawn to the point of tangency. So, $m\angle HJF = m\angle HGF = 90°$.

2. $m\angle MNQ = $ _____ °

   $\overline{QN}$ ____ $\overline{QP}$

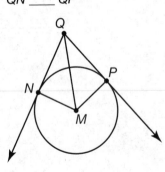

3. Explain how the SAS Congruency Theorem can be used to show that, in the figure at the left, $\triangle QNM \cong \triangle QPM$. Use complete sentences in your answer.

10.6 Gears

Arc Length

Students should be able to answer this question after Lesson 10.6:

■ How is the length of an arc determined?

Directions

Read Question 1 and its solution. Then complete Questions 2 and 3.

1. The radius of a circle is 5 centimeters. Find the circumference.

   Step 1 Circumference is the distance around a circle. The formula for circumference is $C = \pi d$, where d is the diameter of the circle. If the radius is 5 centimeters then the diameter is 10 centimeters. $C = 10\pi$ centimeters

2. The diameter of a circle is 6 centimeters. Find the circumference.

3. The radius of a circle is 7 centimeters. Find the circumference.

Read Question 4 and its solution. Then complete Question 5.

4. The radius of circle T is 7 centimeters and $m\angle RTS = 100°$. Find the arc length of $\overarc{RS}$.

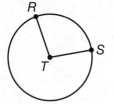

   Step 1 Find the circumference. $C = 14\pi$ centimeters.

   Step 2 Because $m\angle RTS = 100°$ and $\angle RTS$ is a central angle, $m\overarc{RS} = 100°$.

   The arc length of $\overarc{RS}$ is $\dfrac{100°}{360°} \cdot 14\pi$, or $\dfrac{35\pi}{9}$ centimeters.

5. The radius of circle V is 10 centimeters and $m\angle WVU = 130°$. Find the $m\overarc{WU}$.

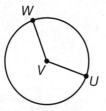

© 2008 Carnegie Learning, Inc.

Chapter 10 ■ Homework Helper **75**

Students should be able to answer these questions after Lesson 10.7:

- How is the area of a sector determined?
- How is the area of a segment determined?

Directions

Read Question 1 and its solution. Then complete Questions 2 and 3.

1. In the figure shown below, $m\angle ZAB = 90°$ and the radius is 5 centimeters. Find the area of the sector.

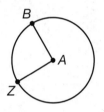

Step 1 Calculate the area of the entire circle. $A = \pi r^2 = \pi(5)^2 = 25\pi$ square centimeters.

Step 2 Find the portion of the circle contained by the sector.

$$\frac{90°}{360°} = \frac{1}{4}$$

Find the area of the sector.

$$\left(\frac{1}{4}\right)(25\pi) = 6.25\pi$$

The area of the sector is 6.25π square centimeters.

2. In the figure shown below, $m\angle ZAB = 100°$ and the radius is 8 centimeters. Find the area of the sector.

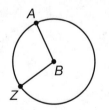

3. In the figure shown below, $m\angle ECD = 120°$ and the radius is 2 centimeters. Find the area of the sector.

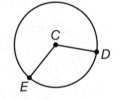

Wheelchair Ramps

The Tangent Ratio

Students should be able to answer these questions after Lesson 11.1:

- How is tangent used to represent angle ratios?
- How is the tangent ratio used to solve problem situations?

Directions

Read Question 1 and its solution. Then complete Questions 2 and 3.

1. In the figure at the right, $m\angle Z = 30°$ and $AY = 5$ feet. Find $\overline{ZY}$.

   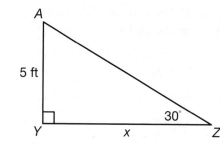

   Step 1 Write an equation by using the tangent ratio.

   $$\tan Z = \frac{\text{length of side opposite } \angle Z}{\text{length of side adjacent } \angle Z}$$

   $$\tan 30° = \frac{5}{x}$$

   Step 2 Solve the equation.

   $$\tan 30° = \frac{5}{x}$$

   $$x \tan 30° = 5$$

   $$x = \frac{5}{\tan 30°}$$

   $$x \approx 8.66 \text{ feet}$$

   The length of $\overline{ZY}$ is about 8.66 feet.

2. In the figure shown below, $m\angle E = 40°$ and $GF = 10$ meters. Find $\overline{EF}$.

   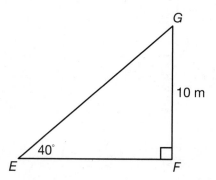

3. In the figure shown below, $m\angle J = 38°$ and $IJ = 7$ centimeters. Find $\overline{HI}$.

   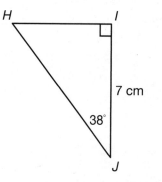

11.2 Golf Club Design
The Sine Ratio

Students should be able to answer these questions after Lesson 11.2:

■ How is sine used to represent angle ratios?

■ How is the sine ratio used to solve problem situations?

Directions

Read Question 1 and its solution. Then complete Questions 2 and 3.

1. A ladder is placed against a wall so that the top of the ladder is 12 feet above the ground and the angle formed between the ladder and the floor is 40°. How long is the ladder?

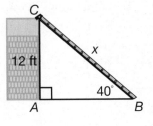

Step 1 Write an equation by using the sine ratio.

$$\sin B = \frac{\text{length of side opposite } \angle B}{\text{length of hypotenuse}}$$

$$\sin 40° = \frac{12}{x}$$

Step 2 Solve the equation.

$$\sin 40° = \frac{12}{x}$$

$$x \sin 40° = 12$$

$$x = \frac{12}{\sin 40°}$$

$$x \approx 18.67 \text{ feet}$$

The length of the ladder is about 18.67 feet.

11

© 2008 Carnegie Learning, Inc.

2. In the figure shown below, $m\angle C = 20°$ and $AB = 4$ feet. Find CB.

C
20°

A 4 ft B

3. In the figure shown below, $m\angle D = 30°$ and $DF = 8$ inches. Find EF.

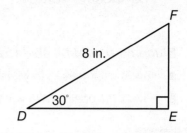

F

8 in.

30°

D   E

11

Attaching a Guy Wire
The Cosine Ratio

Students should be able to answer these questions after Lesson 11.3:

■ How is cosine used to represent angle ratios?

■ How is the cosine ratio used to solve problem situations?

Directions

Read Question 1 and its solution. Then complete Questions 2 and 3.

1. A kite is being flown at a 50° angle with the ground. The string is 20 feet long. What is the horizontal distance of the kite?

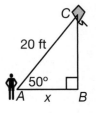

Step 1 Write an equation by using the cosine ratio.

$$\cos A = \frac{\text{length of side adjacent } \angle A}{\text{length of hypotenuse}}$$

$$\cos 50° = \frac{x}{20}$$

Step 2 Solve the equation.

$$\cos 50° = \frac{x}{20}$$

$$20 \cos 50° = x$$

$$12.86 \text{ feet} \approx x$$

The horizontal distance of the kite is about 12.86 feet.

2. In the figure shown below, $m\angle C = 30°$ and $AC = 9$ meters. Find CB.

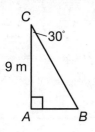

3. In the figure shown below, $m\angle D = 35°$ and $DF = 11$ millimeters. Find ED.

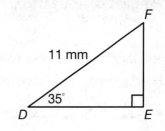

11

Using a Clinometer
Angles of Elevation and Depression

Students should be able to answer this question after Lesson 11.4:

■ How are problems involving the angle of depression or elevation solved?

Read Question 1 and its solution. Then complete Questions 2 and 3.

1. A clinometer measures the angle of elevation from you to the top of a building to be 60°. If you are standing approximately 50 feet away from the building, approximately how tall is the building?

    Step 1 Decide which trigonometric function should be used and solve the appropriate equation. Because you know the adjacent side and are trying to find the opposite side, use the tangent ratio.

    $$\tan A = \frac{\text{length of the side opposite } \angle A}{\text{length of side adjacent } \angle A}$$

    $$\tan 60° = \frac{x}{50}$$

    $$50 \tan 60° = x$$

    $$86.60 \text{ feet} \approx x$$

    The building is about 86.60 feet tall.

2. You are observing a hot air balloon floating in the distance. Its angle of elevation is measured to be 40°. If the vertical distance from the balloon to the ground is approximately 150 feet, what is the horizontal distance from you to where the balloon would land if it came straight down?

3. While hiking, you come to a stream that you may have to swim across. To estimate the distance that you will have to swim, you climb to the top of a tree that is approximately 25 feet high at the edge of the stream. The clinometer measures an angle of depression of 15° to a point on the bank at the other side of the stream. Find the horizontal distance that you will have to swim to cross the stream.

Replacement for a Carpenter's Square

Inscribed Polygons

Students should be able to answer this question after Lesson 12.1:

■ What are the properties of triangles and quadrilaterals inscribed in a circle?

Directions

Read Questions 1 and 2 and their solutions. Then complete Questions 3 and 4.

1. Find the measure of $\overset{\frown}{AEC}$ and $m\angle ADC$.

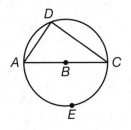

Step 1 Because $\overline{AC}$ is a diameter, $m\overset{\frown}{AEC} = 180°$.

Step 2 Angle ADC intercepts $\overset{\frown}{AEC}$. An inscribed angle measures half the intercepted arc. So, $m\angle ACD = 90°$.

2. $m\angle K + m\angle N = $ _____°

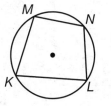

Step 1 When a quadrilateral is inscribed in a circle, opposite angles are supplementary because the arcs intercept the entire circle. $m\angle K + m\angle N = 180°$

3. Find the measure of $\overset{\frown}{HJF}$ and $m\angle HIF$.

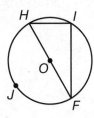

4. $m\angle R + m\angle P = $ _____°

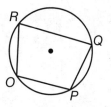

12

Students should be able to answer these questions after Lesson 12.2:

■ How are polyhedrons formed by nets?

■ How are nets drawn?

■ How are nets used to determine surface area?

Directions

Read Question 1 and its solution. Then complete Questions 2 and 3.

1. Draw a net of the polyhedron and determine its surface area.

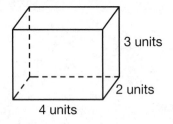

3 units

2 units

4 units

Step 1 Draw a net.

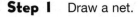

Step 2 To find the surface area, find the sum of the areas of each surface.

Bottom: $(4)(2) = 8$

Top: $(4)(2) = 8$

Front: $(4)(3) = 12$

Back: $(4)(3) = 12$

Side: $(2)(3) = 6$

Side: $(2)(3) = 6$

Total surface area $= 8 + 8 + 12 + 12 + 6 + 6 = 52$ square units.

12

2. The square pyramid has a base length of 4 units and a slant height of 6 units. Draw a net and find the surface area.

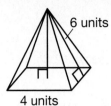

6 units

4 units

3. The cylinder has a height of 10 inches and a diameter of 4 inches. Draw a net and find the surface area. Use 3.14 for π.

Hint: To draw a net, imagine a coffee can. The top and bottom will be circles and the label, when unfolded, is in the shape of a rectangle.

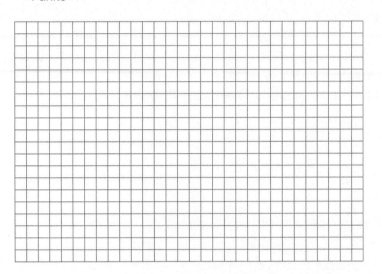

4 in.

10 in.

12

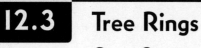

12.3   Tree Rings
Cross Sections

Students should be able to answer these questions after Lesson 12.3:

■ What shapes are produced by various cross sections?

■ What shapes are produced by the intersection of various solids and planes?

Directions

Read Question 1 and its solution. Then complete Questions 2 through 4.

1. What is the cross section of the cube below?

    Step 1   The cross section of the cube is a two-dimensional horizontal slice of the cube. A slice of the cube is the shape of a square.

2. What is the cross section of a sphere when a plane intersects it horizontally as shown below?

    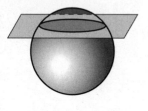

3. Sketch a plane horizontally intersecting a triangular prism. What shape is the cross section?

4. Sketch a plane vertically intersecting a triangular prism. What shape is the cross section?

12

12.4 Minerals and Crystals
Polyhedra and Euler's Formula

Students should be able to answer these questions after Lesson 12.4:

- How can the number of faces, edges, and vertices in polyhedra be determined?
- What is Euler's Formula and how does it relate to polyhedra?

Directions

Read Question 1 and its solution. Then complete Questions 2 though 4.

1. For the cube below, determine the number of faces, edges, and vertices. Verify your answers using Euler's Formula.

Step 1 A face is an outer surface of an object. The cube has 6 faces. An edge is a line segment formed by the intersection of two faces. The cube has 12 edges. A vertex is the point where three or more edges meet (a corner). The cube has 8 vertices.

Step 2 The calculations satisfy Euler's Formula.

$$E + 2 = V + F$$
$$12 + 2 = 8 + 6$$

2. A regular pyramid has 6 edges and 4 faces. Use Euler's Formula to determine the number of vertices that the regular pyramid has.

3. A regular dodecahedron has 12 faces and 20 vertices. Use Euler's Formula to determine the number of edges that the regular dodecahedron has.

4. Draw a regular pyramid (tetrahedron). Use the diagram to determine the number of edges, faces, and vertices. Verify your answer using Euler's Formula.

12

Isometric Drawing
Compositions

Students should be able to answer these questions after Lesson 12.5:

■ Given an isometric drawing, how can the top, side, and front views be drawn?

■ How is an isometric drawing created given the top, front, and side views?

Directions

Read Question 1 and its solution. Then complete Questions 2 and 3.

1. An isometric drawing is shown below. Draw the top view, front view, and side view.

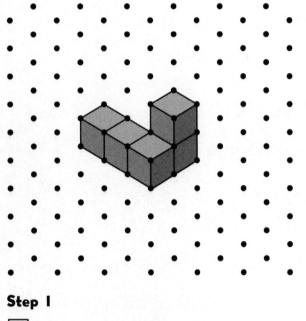

Step 1

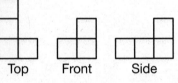

Top   Front   Side

2. An isometric drawing is shown below. Draw the top view, front view, and side view.

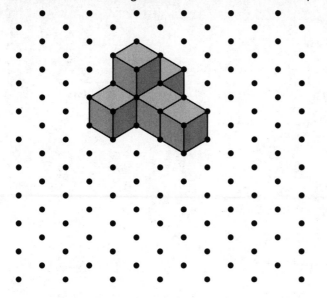

3. Create an isometric drawing given the top view, front view, and side view shown below.

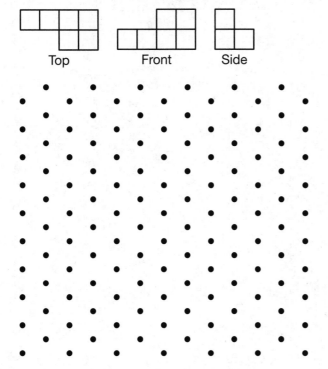

Top   Front   Side

12

Answers

Chapter 1

Lesson 1.1

2. Perimeter = 56 feet
   Area = 192 square feet (tiles)

3. Perimeter = 42 feet
   Area = 104 square feet (tiles)

4. A rectangular patio that is 10 feet by 10 feet
   will require the least amount of fence.

Lesson 1.2

2. 88 square feet   3. 117 square feet

4. 144 square feet   5. 90 square feet

Lesson 1.3

2. 5 square feet   3. 5 square yards

5. $b = 5$ 6. $b = 7$ 7. $h = 16$

Lesson 1.4

2. 20 square inches

3. 100 square centimeters

4. 13 square meters

6. 10 centimeters

7. 12 yards

Lesson 1.5

2. 60 square feet

3. 120 square centimeters

4. 1584 square inches

Lesson 1.6

2. 43.96 centimeters

3. 37.68 inches

5. 50.24 square centimeters

6. 314 square inches

Lesson 1.7

2. 21 square centimeters

3. 47.5 square feet

Chapter 2

Lesson 2.1

2. 90 cubic inches; 126 square inches

3. 10 cubic inches; 34 square inches

4. 27 cubic centimeters; 54 square centimeters

Lesson 2.2

2. 64 cubic inches

3. 70 cubic centimeters

Lesson 2.3

2. 1428 square inches

3. 122 square inches

Lesson 2.4

2. 2400 cubic feet

3. 30 cubic feet

Lesson 2.5

2. 96 square meters

3. 108 square centimeters

Lesson 2.6

2. 113.04 cubic centimeters

3. 254.34 cubic yards

5. 25.12 square centimeters

6. 628 square feet

Lesson 2.7

2. 113.04 cubic inches; 239.268 square inches

3. 50.24 cubic meters; 113.04 square meters

Lesson 2.8

2. 267.947 cubic centimeters;
   200.96 square centimeters

3. 3052.08 cubic millimeters;
   1017.36 square millimeters

Chapter 3

Lesson 3.1

2. Line CD; $\overleftrightarrow{CD}$; or Line DC; $\overleftrightarrow{DC}$

3. Segment MN; $\overline{MN}$ or Segment NM; $\overline{NM}$

4. acute   **5.** obtuse   **6.** right

Lesson 3.2

2. complement: 25°; supplement: 115°

4. $m\angle CBA = m\angle EBD = 30°$; $m\angle CBE = 150°$; $\angle CBA$ and $\angle EBD$ are vertical angles; $\angle CBE$ and $\angle EBD$ form a linear pair

Lesson 3.3

2. 80°   **3.** 76°   **5.** 100°

Lesson 3.4

2. the triangle is scalene and obtuse

3. the triangle is isosceles and right

4. the triangle is isosceles and obtuse

Lesson 3.5

2. $2 < x < 8$ **3.** $2 < x < 14$ **4.** DC, ED, CE

Chapter 4

Lesson 4.1

2. 11   **3.** 28   **4.** $3\sqrt{3}$ **5.** $5\sqrt{3}$

6. $7\sqrt{2}$ **7.** $\dfrac{\sqrt{6}}{6}$ **8.** $\dfrac{8\sqrt{5}}{5}$

9. $\dfrac{9\sqrt{3}}{6} = \dfrac{3\sqrt{3}}{2}$ **10.** $\dfrac{4\sqrt{6}}{2} = 2\sqrt{6}$

Lesson 4.2

2. $b = 21$ **3.** $c = 17$ **4.** $a = 8$

5. $c \approx 14.1$ **6.** $a \approx 12.4$ **7.** $b \approx 29.2$

Lesson 4.3

2. $c = 21\sqrt{2}$ ft; 220.5 sq ft

3. $a = 17\sqrt{2}$ cm; 289 sq cm

4. $b = \dfrac{25\sqrt{2}}{2}$ in.; 156.25 sq in

Lesson 4.4

2. $c = 30$ m; $b = 15\sqrt{3}$ m; $\dfrac{225}{2}\sqrt{3}$ square meters

3. $a = \dfrac{9}{2}$ mm; $b = \dfrac{9}{2}\sqrt{3}$ mm; $\dfrac{81}{8}\sqrt{3}$ square mm

4. $a = 9\sqrt{3}$ ft; $c = 18\sqrt{3}$ ft; $\dfrac{243}{2}\sqrt{3}$ square feet

Lesson 4.5

2. $\sqrt{314} \approx 17.7$ **3.** $\sqrt{125} \approx 11.2$

4. $\sqrt{160} \approx 12.6$ **5.** $x = \pm 6$

Lesson 4.6

2. $(0, -5)$ **3.** $\left(2, \dfrac{13}{2}\right)$

4. $(-3, -7)$ **5.** $x = 9$

Chapter 5

Lesson 5.1

2. Angle Pairs:

Corresponding: $\angle 1$ and $\angle 3$, $\angle 2$ and $\angle 4$, $\angle 5$ and $\angle 7$, $\angle 6$ and $\angle 8$

Alternate Interior: $\angle 3$ and $\angle 7$, $\angle 2$ and $\angle 6$

Alternate Exterior: $\angle 1$ and $\angle 5$, $\angle 4$ and $\angle 8$

Same-Side Interior: $\angle 2$ and $\angle 3$, $\angle 7$ and $\angle 6$

Same-Side Exterior: $\angle 1$ and $\angle 4$, $\angle 5$ and $\angle 8$

Angle Measures:

$m\angle 1 = 100°$, $m\angle 2 = 80°$, $m\angle 3 = 100°$, $m\angle 4 = 80°$, $m\angle 5 = 100°$, $m\angle 6 = 80°$, $m\angle 7 = 100°$, $m\angle 8 = 80°$

Lesson 5.2

2. $m\angle 4 = 75°$

4. Transitive Property

5. Addition Property

6. Subtraction Property

Answers

Lesson 5.3

2. 60°; sample answer: Angles 1 and 4 are congruent by the Alternate Exterior Angles Postulate.

3. 120°; sample answer: Angles 2 and 5 are congruent by the Corresponding Angles Theorem.

4. 60°; sample answer: Angles 1 and 6 are congruent by the Corresponding Angles Theorem.

6. Definition of congruent angles

7. Vertical angles are congruent

8. Transitive Property of Equality

9. Definition of supplementary angles

Lesson 5.4

2. Parallel Line: sample answer: $3x + 1$;

   Perpendicular Line: sample answer: $-\frac{1}{3}x + 1$

3. Parallel Line: sample answer: $-\frac{2}{3}x + 2$;

   Perpendicular Line: sample answer: $\frac{3}{2}x + 2$

5. Horizontal: sample answer: $y = -6$; Vertical: sample answer: $x = 3$

Lesson 5.5

1. Slope of $\overline{BC} = 2$; $BC = 8\sqrt{5}$

   Slope of $\overline{CA} = -\frac{1}{2}$; $CA = 16\sqrt{5}$

2. Midpoint of $\overline{AB}$: (0, 0)

   Midpoint of $\overline{BC}$: (16, −8)

   Midpoint of $\overline{CA}$: (−4, −8)

3. Slope of $\overline{DE} = -\frac{1}{2}$; $DE = 8\sqrt{5}$;

   Slope of $\overline{EF} = 0$; $EF = 20$;

   Slope of $\overline{FD} = 2$; $FD = 4\sqrt{5}$

Lesson 5.6

2. 65°   3. 60°   5. 11 in.   6. 26 cm

Lesson 5.7

2. 10 cm   3. 10 mm

4. obtuse triangle; right triangle

Chapter 6

Section 6.1

1. b. Vertical Reflection Line

   c. Vertical Reflection Line

   d. Horizontal Reflection Line

   e. No reflection line can be drawn

3. *x*-axis: (−3, −5); *y*-axis: (3, 5); $y = x$: (5, −3)

4. *x*-axis: (5, -8); *y*-axis: (−5, 8); $y = x$: (8, 5)

5. *x*-axis: (0 −2); *y*-axis: (0, 2); $y = x$: (2, 0)

Lesson 6.2

2. 90° counterclockwise: (−4, −2),
   180°: (2, −4),
   90° clockwise: (4, 2)

3. 90° counterclockwise: (3, 4),
   180°: (−4, 3),
   90° clockwise: (−3, −4)

Lesson 6.3

2. The vertices will be (4, 0), (7, 5), and (11, 0).

4. The triangle will move 2 units to the left and 3 units up. The new vertices will be (−1, 5), (−4, 8), and (−2, −4).

Lesson 6.4

2. The image will be smaller. The new coordinates are (−1, −0.5), (2.5, −0.5), (−1, 2), and (2.5, 2).

4. The scale factor will be $\frac{2}{5} = 0.4$.

Lesson 6.5

2. The figure has 6 lines of symmetry.

3. The figure has 1 line of symmetry—a vertical line.

5. Yes.

6. No.

Answers

Chapter 7

Section 7.1

2. $\dfrac{10}{6} = \dfrac{5}{3}$ **3.** $\dfrac{10}{24} = \dfrac{5}{12}$

5. $\dfrac{8}{24} = \dfrac{x}{200}$; $x \approx 67$ students

Section 7.2

2. $\dfrac{16}{4} = \dfrac{30}{x}$; $x = 7.5$ inches

3. $\dfrac{10}{x} = \dfrac{8}{4}$; $x = 5$ feet

5. Yes, she did use the correct scale factor

because $\dfrac{16.5}{1.5} = 11$.

Section 7.3

2. Yes, because of the SAS Similarity Theorem.

3. No, the triangles are not similar. You cannot use the SAS Theorem because the angle is not included between the sides in the second triangle.

Section 7.4

2. $\dfrac{10}{x} = \dfrac{15}{120}$; $x = 80$ ft

Section 7.5

2. a. The ratio of the radii is $\dfrac{2}{1}$.

  b. Surface area of larger figure:

  $2\pi r^2 + 2\pi rh = 2\pi(4) + 2\pi(2)(10)$

  $\qquad = 8\pi + 40\pi = 48\pi$

  Surface area of smaller figure:

  $2\pi r^2 + 2\pi rh = 2\pi(1) + 2\pi(1)(5)$

  $\qquad = 2\pi + 10\pi = 12\pi$

  The ratio of the surface areas is

  $\dfrac{48\pi}{12\pi} = \dfrac{4}{1}$.

  c. Volume of the larger figure:

  $\pi r^2 h = \pi(4)(10) = 40\pi$

  Volume of the smaller figure:

  $\pi r^2 h = \pi(1)(5) = 5\pi$

  The ratio of the volumes is

  $\dfrac{40\pi}{5\pi} = \dfrac{8}{1}$.

3. a. The ratio of the lengths is $\dfrac{6}{3} = 2$.

  b. Surface area of larger figure:

  $(6)(6)(6 \text{ sides}) = 216$ square millimeters

  Surface area of smaller figure:

  $(3)(3)(6 \text{ sides}) = 54$ square millimeters

  The ratio of the surface areas is $\dfrac{216}{54} = 4$.

  c. Volume of the larger figure:

  $(6)(6)(6) = 216$ cubic millimeters

  Volume of the smaller figure:

  $(3)(3)(3) = 27$ cubic millimeters

  The ratio of the volumes is $\dfrac{216}{27} = 8$.

Chapter 8

Section 8.1

2. $\overline{GH}$ and $\overline{JK}$, $\overline{GI}$ and $\overline{JL}$, $\overline{HI}$ and $\overline{KL}$, $m\angle G$ and $m\angle J$, $m\angle H$ and $m\angle K$, $m\angle I$ and $m\angle L$

3. Congruent triangles will be alike in that all corresponding sides and angles are congruent. They are different in that they may be oriented differently.

4. Similar triangles have the same shape and same proportions. However, they may be different sizes.

6. $m\angle C = 60°$, $m\angle X = 70°$, $m\angle Y = 50°$, $m\angle Z = 60°$

Answers

Lesson 8.2

2. Point N is the midpoint so $\overline{LN} \cong \overline{NO}$ and $\overline{MN} \cong \overline{NP}$. The triangles are congruent by SSS.

4. Vertical angles are congruent so $\angle VJU \cong \angle WJX$. The triangles are congruent by SAS.

Lesson 8.3

2. With the given information, and the fact that $\overline{CA} \cong \overline{CA}$ (reflexive), you can show that the triangles are congruent using the ASA Congruence Theorem.

4. Yes, you have enough information to use the AAS Congruence Theorem.

Lesson 8.4

2. Method 1: Because $\overline{CB}$ and $\overline{AD}$ are parallel, $\angle CBD$ and $\angle ADB$ are congruent (alternate interior angles). From this you can determine that the triangles are congruent using the ASA Congruence Theorem.

Method 2: Both triangles share $\overline{BD}$, which is the hypotenuse of both right triangles. From this fact, you can use the Hypotenuse-Leg Congruence Theorem to show that the triangles are congruent.

Lesson 8.5

2. The total area increases as the number of triangles increases.

3. The area of each new triangle decreases as the number of triangles increases.

4. The side length changes by a factor of $\frac{1}{3}$.

5. The perimeter increases.

Chapter 9

Lesson 9.1

2. F   **3.** F   **4.** T   **5.** B   **6.** G

7. A   **8.** D   **9.** E   **10.** F

Lesson 9.2

2. It is a 90° angle because the diagonals of a kite are perpendicular.

3. They are congruent because diagonal BD is the perpendicular bisector of diagonal AC.

5. The diagonals are congruent. The diagonals of an isosceles trapezoid are congruent.

Lesson 9.3

2. $m\angle Q = 80°, m\angle R = 100°$

4. $AB = 4$ cm, $m\angle B = 120°, m\angle BAC = 30°$

Lesson 9.4

2. $BA = 4$ meters, $AD = 7$ meters, $BD = \sqrt{65}$ meters

4. True because all squares are parallelograms.

5. False because a square must have four equal side lengths, but a rectangle may have four equal side lengths, or two pairs of opposite sides that are equal in length.

6. True because a rectangle has opposite sides that are equal in length and four right angles. This is also true in a square.

Lesson 9.5

2. $(12 - 2)(180) = 1800°$

4. $\dfrac{1800}{12} = 150°$

5. $135n = 180n - 360$

$-45n = -360$

$n = 8°$

Lesson 9.6

2. 360°   **3.** 360°   **4.** $(5 - 2)(180) = 540°$

Lesson 9.7

2. square   **3.** square

Chapter 10

Lesson 10.1

2. Answers may vary. Answers should be similar to Question 1.

Lesson 10.2

2. 70°; 35°   **3.** 90°; 90°

Lesson 10.3

5. 100°   **6.** 45°   **7.** 65°   **8.** 120°

Lesson 10.4

2. $m\overset{\frown}{CB} = 80°$

3. Yes, by the SSS Theorem. Along with the given information, $\overline{DA} \cong \overline{BA}$ (they are both radii) and $\overline{AE} \cong \overline{AE}$ (reflexive).

Lesson 10.5

2. $m\angle MNQ = 90°$ (tangent); $\overline{QN} \cong \overline{QP}$

3. $\overline{QN} \cong \overline{QP}$ (tangent segments from the same exterior point are congruent); $\overline{MN} \cong \overline{MP}$ (they are both radii); $m\angle MNQ = m\angle QPM = 90°$. Therefore, you can use the SAS Congruence Theorem.

Lesson 10.6

2. $C = 6\pi$ centimeters

3. $C = (2 \cdot 7)\pi = 14\pi$ centimeters

5. $C = (2 \cdot 10)\pi = 20\pi$ centimeters

$$\left(\frac{130°}{360°}\right)(20\pi) = \frac{65\pi}{9} \text{ cm}$$

Lesson 10.7

2. $A = (\pi)(8^2) = 64\pi$ square centimeters
Sector:

$$\left(\frac{100°}{360°}\right)(64\pi) = \frac{160\pi}{9} \text{ square centimeters}$$

3. $A = (\pi)(2^2) = 4\pi$ square centimeters

Sector: $\left(\frac{120°}{360°}\right)(4\pi) = \frac{4\pi}{3}$ square centimeters

Chapter 11

Lesson 11.1

2. $\tan 40° = \frac{10}{x}$

$x \tan 40° = 10$

$$x = \frac{10}{\tan 40°}$$

$x \approx 11.92$ meters

3. $\tan 38° = \frac{x}{7}$

$7 \tan 38° = x$

$5.47 \text{ cm} \approx x$

Lesson 11.2

2. $\sin 20° = \frac{4}{x}$

$x \sin 20° = 4$

$$x = \frac{4}{\sin 20°}$$

$x \approx 11.70$ feet

3. $\sin 30° = \frac{x}{8}$

$8 \sin 30° = x$

$4 \text{ inches} = x$

Lesson 11.3

2. $\cos 30° = \frac{9}{x}$

$x \cos 30° = 9$

$$x = \frac{9}{\cos 30°}$$

$x \approx 10.39$ m

3. $\cos 35° = \frac{x}{11}$

$11 \cos 35° = x$

$9.01 \text{ mm} \approx x$

Lesson 11.4

2. $\tan 40° = \frac{150}{x}$

$x \tan 40° = 150$

$$x = \frac{150}{\tan 40°}$$

$x \approx 178.76$ ft

Answers

3. $\tan 75° = \dfrac{x}{25}$

$25 \tan 75° = x$

$93.30 \text{ ft} \approx x$

Chapter 12

Lesson 12.1

3. $m\widehat{HJF} = 180°$, $m\angle HIF = 90°$ **4.** $180°$

Lesson 12.2

2. Surface Area =

$(4)(4) + 4\left(\dfrac{1}{2} \cdot 4 \cdot 6\right) = 64$ square units

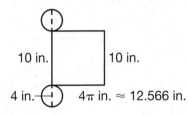

4 units

6 units

3. Surface Area $= 2\pi r^2 + 2\pi rh$

$= 2(\pi)(2^2) + 2\pi(2)(10)$

≈ 150.72 square inches

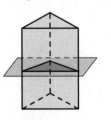

10 in.   10 in.

4 in. 4π in. ≈ 12.566 in.

Lesson 12.3

2. The cross section of a sphere is a circle.

3. The cross section is a triangle.

4. The cross section is a rectangle.

Lesson 12.4

2. $E + 2 = V + F$

$6 + 2 = V + 4$

$8 = V + 4$

$V = 4$

3. $E + 2 = 20 + 12$

$E + 2 = 32$

$E = 30$

4.

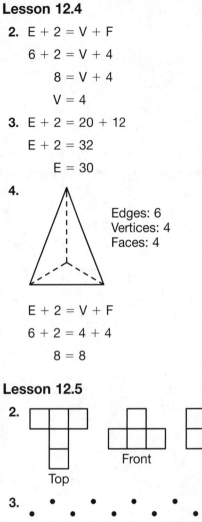

Edges: 6
Vertices: 4
Faces: 4

$E + 2 = V + F$

$6 + 2 = 4 + 4$

$8 = 8$

Lesson 12.5

2.

Top   Front   Side

3.

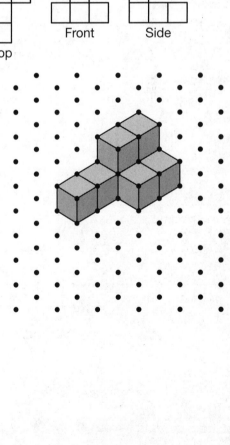

© 2008 Carnegie Learning, Inc.